In these pages, you will meet some of the cleverest, most intriguing posers ever devised.

Try your hand at these stumpers, or share them with a group of friends. This is a great book for a party, or for a beach social, as well as for personal enjoyment on a train, a plane, or while in an easy chair.

Some of the puzzles are relatively easy; some are real brain-twisters, most require only good common sense.

So whether you're a novice or an old hand at the puzzle game, this book will provide countless hours of wit-sharpening entertainment.

TED PARKER MALONEY

Clever Puzzles
FOR
Clever People

A HART BOOK

A & W VISUAL LIBRARY
New York

PUBLISHED BY
A & W PUBLSHERS, INC.
95 MADISON AVENUE
NEW YORK, NEW YORK 10016

LIBRARY OF CONGRESS CATALOG CARD NO. 79-52808

ISBN: 0-89104-151-6

Printed in Canada

CONTENTS

THE HONEY JARS

A beekeeper has devised a system for keeping tabs on his jars of honey. He has arranged the jars on his shelves so that he has 18 quarts of honey on each shelf. The jars are in three sizes.

Can you tell how much each size contains?

Answer on page 119

BEAR UP!

WHAT IS THE ANSWER TO
JOHN MCJOHN'S QUESTION?

Answer on page 119

KILLED IN ACTION

Five friends named Jones, Stacey, Young, Lewis, and Smith were involved in a battle, and one of the men was killed. The following facts are known:

(1) Jones was an ordained Catholic priest.

(2) The wife of the slain man was the sister of Mrs. Lewis.

(3) Mrs. Smith's beautiful daughter died of infantile paralysis.

(4) Stacey was sorry that Young did not return on the same boat with him.

(5) Mrs. Lewis always regretted that she had never had a niece or nephew.

Which man was killed in the battle?

Answer on page 120

APPOINTMENT IN ABILENE

Percy Poppon had an appointment in Abilene at two o'clock in the afternoon. If he left his home and traveled at 15 miles per hour, he would arrive at one o'clock; if he traveled at 10 miles per hour he would not arrive until three o'clock. *What was the distance from his home to Abilene?*

Answer on page 120

THE WHIFFLEBIRD

THAT POOR WHIFFLEBIRD HAS NO MORE LEAVES LEFT TO EAT FROM THAT TREE. THE FIRST DAY HE ATE ONLY ONE LEAF. THE NEXT DAY HE ATE DOUBLE THE NUMBER OF LEAVES HE HAD EATEN THE FIRST DAY, AND THE THIRD DAY DOUBLE THE NUMBER OF LEAVES HE HAD EATEN THE SECOND DAY. AND SO ON FOR THIRTY DAYS UNTIL ALL THE LEAVES WERE GONE.

AND ON WHAT DAY WERE HALF THE LEAVES GONE?

ON WHAT DAY HAD THE WHIFFLEBIRD EATEN
EXACTLY HALF THE LEAVES ON THE TREE?

Answer on page 121

THE MARKED FOREHEADS

A professor, wishing to determine who was the brightest among three of his cleverest students, named Alex, Joe, and Tom, arranged a little experiment. He had the three of them sit around a small circular table, each one facing the other two. Explaining that he was going to paste a little label on the forehead of each, he bade his three boys close their eyes. He told them that the labels would either be marked with a blue cross or a green cross. The challenge, he continued, consisted merely of this: that if any one of the students saw a green cross he should raise his hand, and that as soon as a student knew what color cross his forehead was marked with he should fold his arms on his chest.

While their eyes were shut, the professor proceeded to label each with a *green cross.* He then told the boys that all was set. They opened their eyes and each immediately raised his hand. After a lapse of a few minutes Alex folded his arms. The professor asked him how he was marked. Alex answered "Green." *Can you explain the reasoning by which he made his deduction?*

Answer on page 121

THE FISHERMAN

Two fishermen caught a large fish and wished to know its weight, but did not have a scale on hand. So they set a plank up as a see-saw, and with one fisherman standing on each end, they moved the plank until it was exactly balanced. Keeping the plank in the same position, they then changed places, and the lighter man put the fish on his side of the plank. This brought the balance exactly right again. The weights of the fishermen were 120 and 150 lbs. *What was the weight of the fish?*

Answer on page 122

IN COLD BLOOD

Two sisters were married. The two couples jointly occupied a single apartment. The men, apart from being brothers-in-law, were otherwise unrelated. One night, while both men were asleep, one of the girls said to her sister: "Come with me." She led her into the chamber where the two men were sleeping, and having approached her own husband, she drew a dagger and plunged it into his vitals. He awoke, shouting in his death agony: "You are murdering me!" His brother-in-law, awakened by his cries, heard the woman announce coldly, "Yes, that's what I intend to do," and saw her again plunge the poniard up to its hilt into the victim's heart.

All the foregoing facts were established at the trial, not only by the evidence of the accused's sister and brother-in-law, but by the confession of the defendant herself. The jury duly brought in a verdict of "Guilty of murder in the first degree."

The judge stated that the verdict was unimpeachable, and while deploring the depravity of the defendant, he nevertheless stated to a crowded courtroom that under the law he found it impossible to pronounce sentence upon her. The accused then walked off scot-free.

Now take it for granted that the trial was held in due conformity with legal requirements. Take it for granted that the verdict could not be set aside for any legal technicality, and furthermore, take it for granted that the judge was fully competent and exercised unimpeachable judgment. In short, the difficulty did not arise from any deficiencies in either the processes of the law or the presiding tribunal. The dilemma arose solely out of the circumstances of the case. *What logical reason could the judge have for refusing to pronounce sentence upon the murderer?*

Answer on page 123

THE CYCLISTS AND THE FLY

Two cyclists, 20 miles apart, start at the same instant and ride towards each other along a straight road at a speed of 10 miles per hour. At the same instant a fly on the forehead of one of the riders starts to fly at 15 miles per hour toward the other rider, alights on his forehead, and then immediately flies back to the first rider. The fly travels back and forth over the continuously decreasing distance between the two riders until the two riders meet. *How far has the fly flown when all its journeys are added together?*

Answer on page 123

THE LEGIONNAIRES

WHERE DOES EACH LEGIONNAIRE COME FROM:
RENO, MIAMI, BUFFALO, BANGOR, LOS ANGELES?
EACH HAS A DIFFERENT HOME.

Answer on page 123

THE LADY AND THE TIGER

In ancient days, a certain crafty king had a daughter
as beautiful as he was vicious. Her charm and beauty
attracted suitors from the four corners of the earth
who came to sue for her hand.

But the king imposed harsh conditions. Each
suitor was obliged to put up a fortune, if he even
dared to try to win the maiden, a fortune which became forfeit to the crown if the suitor was unsuccess-
ful. Then the candidate was given a number of difficult feats to perform. If he succeeded in overcoming
these trials of strength and courage, he would then
be led to a box which contained two slips of paper.
On one there was written the name of the princess;
on the other, the word *Tiger*. If he drew the slip with

the word *Tiger* on it, he would be thrown into a cage, there to meet a cruel death.

Mathematically, his chances of winning the girl were even; but practically, his chances were nil because the unscrupulous monarch always put into the box two slips of paper on both of which was written the word *Tiger*.

After many suitors had met an untimely death in this manner, the princess had become aware of her father's deceit.

One day, a handsome young man came a-riding to the palace, and she immediately fell in love with him. Since she couldn't bear to see him be torn limb from limb by a vicious tiger, she told him of the king's stratagem and what lay in store for anyone who tried for her hand.

Undaunted, the young man announced that he was a suitor, and accomplished the feats of strength and other tasks set for him. Then he was led away to the box which held his fate.

But somehow he contrived to outwit the king. *How did he do it?*

Answer on page 124

THE FIRED WATCHMAN

Mr. Peabody was president of the Star Bottle Works. On Tuesday, at a directors' meeting, it was decided that Mr. Peabody should go to Chicago to close a large contract then pending. The office force soon learned of the projected trip, and the news soon leaked through to Jim Casey, night watchman of the bottle factory.

Jim, all in a tremor, hurried over to the main office and battled his way into the presidential office. Face to face with the president, he blurted out what was on his mind.

"Mr. Peabody," he said, "I heard you were going to Chicago. Don't do it, Mr. Peabody, please don't do it. I had a terrible dream last night that you were shot in Chicago by a gangster."

Just then Peabody's secretary entered to tell him that he would have to hurry to catch his train, whereupon the executive, paying no heed to the pleas of the watchman, grabbed his valise and rushed out.

Four days later, Peabody returned, hale and hearty. The contract had been signed. His first act was to dismiss Casey. *Why?*

Answer on page 124

THE STRANDED TEDDY BEAR

Father takes little Oswald to the zoo. Ozzie is especially attracted by the fierce alligators who lie exposed in the shallow water of a circular moat.

We now interrupt this story with some simple figures: The moat is six feet deep. In the center of it, there is a concrete island, which is exactly 11 feet away from the outer edge of the moat.

Little Ozzie gets sort of bumptious and flings his teddy bear onto the island. He cries his head off, so his Pa decides to do something about the situation.

Scurrying around, Father finds a nine-foot plank and a 10-foot plank, but nothing to nail or bind them together. However, with the aid of these two pieces of wood, he somehow contrives to retrieve the teddy bear 11 feet away. *How does he do it?*

Answer on page 124

THE NOBLES
AND THE SLAVES

WHICH OF THE THREE AFRICANS ARE NOBLES?

Answer on page 125

AT CENTRAL STATION

All the trains from Central Station go to Fogwell. From Fogwell, some go on to Kemp; others, to Banstock and then to Midvale; others, to Greenfields and on to Deane. The fare is $3 to Kemp, Midvale, or Deane; elsewhere, $2.

Dan is in a hurry. He has bought a $2 ticket. The first train is going to Midvale, but Dan does not get on.

What is Dan's destination?

Answer on page 125

DR. LIMEJUICE

A statue of Dr. Limejuice, the temperance reformer, stands in Drinkwell marketplace. The other night two boys of Drinkwell School painted the doctor's nose red. One of them held a lantern, while the other did the actual painting.

The headmaster, having received a report from the police, sent for three boys, Sniggersby, Tittering, and Wallop. He proceeded to ask each of them three questions, putting the questions to the three boys in rotation. The questions, and the answers received, were as follows (but the order in which the boys were questioned is not necessarily that given above):

Headmaster: You are one of the two culprits?

First Boy: No, sir.

Headmaster: You are, then?

Second Boy: Yes, sir.

Headmaster: And you are?

Third Boy: No, sir.

Headmaster: Of those three statements, two at least are untrue?

First Boy: No, sir.

Headmaster (reading): "Sniggersby was holding the lantern." Is that true?

Second Boy: No, sir.

Headmaster (reading): "Tittering painted the statue." Is that true?

Third Boy: No, sir.

Headmaster (reading): "Wallop is not implicated." Is that true?

First Boy: No, sir.

Headmaster (reading): "You can rely on Sniggersby not to tell you a lie." Is that true?

Second Boy: Yes, sir.

Headmaster (reading): "And you can similarly rely on Wallop." Is that true?

Third Boy: Yes, sir.

Each of the suspects has now answered three questions. Wallop has lied twice, and the other two boys have each lied once.

Who held the lantern, and who painted the doctor's nose?

Answer on page 125

RELATIVELY SIMPLE

WHAT RELATION IS ANN TO JOAN?

Answer on page 126

THE TWO CANOES

At precisely the same moment, two boys start paddling their canoes from opposite sides of a river. One boy paddles faster than the other. They meet at a point 410 feet from one of the shores.

After each arrives at his destination, he remains there for 10 minutes. Then he starts on his return trip.

The canoes again meet, this time at a point 230 feet from one of the shores.

What is the exact width of the river?

Answer on page 126

THE HORSE RACE

Three colts were running in a race. Their names were Tally-ho, Sonny Boy, and Regent. Their owners were Mr. Lewis, Mr. Bailey, and Mr. Smith, although not necessarily respectively.

Tally-ho unfortunately broke his ankle at the start of the race.

Mr. Smith owned a brown and white three-year-old.

Sonny Boy had previous winnings of $35,000.

Mr. Bailey lost heavily, although his horse almost won.

The horse that won was black.

This race was the first race run by Mr. Lewis's horse.

What was the name of the horse that won, and who was his owner?

Answer on page 127

THE SOCCER LEAGUE

Four teams—Arsenal, Hotspur, United, and Villa— take part in a soccer competition. Each team plays each of the others once. Two points are awarded for a win and one for a tie.

United scored five points; Hotspur, three points; Villa, one point. Thirteen goals were scored in all, seven of these by the Hotspur; the Arsenal scored no goals at all.

Hotspur beat Villa by four goals to one.

What was the score in the game between Villa and United?

Answer on page 127

LATE FOR TEE

CAN YOU ANSWER JOE'S QUESTION?

Answer on page 128

THE MARINERS

There are three ships, the *Albatross*, the *Americus*, and the *Hispaniola*, on the sea sailing for the ports of Liverpool, New York, and Cherbourg, but not necessarily in that order. The ships are commanded by Captains Brine, Tarr, and Salt.

A few months ago Captain Tarr was the guest of Captain Brine on the *Albatross*.

The *Hispaniola* hit a derelict on her last crossing, and as a result was in dry dock for repairs for seven weeks previous to the present trip.

The *Albatross* has just passed the *Americus* in mid-ocean, and shipped a stowaway back by the *Americus*.

Mrs. Salt, who usually travels with her husband, was yesterday discharged from the hospital where she was treated for a week for a severe attack of ulcers. This unfortunate condition victimized her while she was three days from land and necessitated her immediate removal to the hospital when the ship docked.

The Captain of the *Americus* is preparing a report for his owners, Cartright and Smith, Ltd., of Liverpool, which he will deliver to their offices as soon as his ship docks.

What ship does Captain Tarr command, and to what port is it bound?

Answer on page 129

THE FORTY-TWO BEERS

In Guatelavia, the standard dollar is worth 100¢. In the bordering country of Tinto, the standard dollar is also worth 100¢. In fact, both dollars contain the same gold equivalent and are of exact value.

However, because of conditions of foreign exchange, the Guatelavian dollar is worth only 90¢ in Tinto, while the Tintoese dollar is worth but 90¢ in Guatelavia.

One day a smart Yankee with an enormous thirst drops into a Guatelavian cafe and orders a 10¢ beer. He hands over the single Guatelavian dollar that he has in his pocket, and asks for 90¢ in change in Tintoese money. Since the Tintoese dollar is only worth 90¢ in Guatelavia, the barkeep gives him a full Tintoese dollar.

Whereupon our friend hops across the border and makes for the nearest saloon. He orders a beer and hands the bartender in Tinto a Tintoese dollar—the one he got in Guatelavia—demanding 90¢ change in Guatelavian money. Since, as aforesaid, the Guatelavian dollar is worth only 90¢ in Tinto, he receives a full Guatelavian dollar for his change.

Things look pretty bright for the Yankee, and he keeps up the transaction the whole day long, imbibing exactly 42 beers. When he is done, he finds that he has the same Guatelavian dollar that he started out with.

Now apparently the Guatelavian cafe sold 21 beers at the ordinary price and made a profit; and apparently the Tintoese saloon sold 21 beers with a profit, and evidently the American financial wizard got 42 beers without expending a single penny . . . So the question remains: *Who paid for them there beers?*

Answer on page 129

SCALING THE ORCHARD WALL

A boy wishing to get to the top of an orchard wall found that the ladder he had brought, when placed upright against the wall, just reached to the top. So he pulled the foot of the ladder out exactly 10 feet, and supported it on a box two feet high. The top of the ladder then reached exactly to the top of the wall. *What was the height of the wall?*

Answer on page 130

THE ARTIST'S CANVAS

An artist has an oddly shaped piece of canvas that contains exactly 81 square inches.

The small square piece projecting at the top is one inch on a side. It is attached to a square of 16 square inches, which is in turn attached to a larger square of 64 square inches. The artist wants to make a nine-by-nine square canvas for his painting.

How can he divide the canvas into the smallest number of pieces that will fit together to make a perfect square?

Answer on page 130

THE COMMUTER

CAN YOU TELL HOW MUCH TIME BROWN
SPENT WALKING UNTIL HE MET HIS CAR?

Answer on page 131

THE HORSE TRADER

A horse trader brings a string of horses to a horse fair. As admission charge, he gives up one of his horses. At the fair, he sells one half of those remaining; and on the way out, he is charged one horse as a trading fee.

He proceeds to a second fair where like conditions prevail. There he pays one horse to get in, sells half of the horses he still has on hand, and pays a single horse as trading fee.

And, not content, he proceeds to a third fair. Here again he pays one horse to get in, sells one half of the horses remaining, and is charged a single horse on the way out as a trading fee.

He then has one horse left on which to ride home with his proceeds.

How many horses did he start out with?

Answer on page 131

MURDER IN THE LIBRARY

Mr. Parker was found dead in the library of his home on the evening of January 2, at 7:30 P.M. His death was reported to the police by a night watchman, who, because he was the only person other than the dead man in the immediate vicinity, was questioned by the inspector in charge as follows:

Inspector: What was your first knowledge of Mr. Parker's death?

Watchman: As I was walking past his house, I saw him seated in this chair. As I watched him, he raised a pistol to his head and shot himself.

Inspector: What did you do then?

Watchman: I rushed to the door and rang the bell, but I could get no response.

Inspector: How did you get into the house?

Watchman: I ran around the house trying the windows. I found an unlocked one in the rear and climbed through it.

Inspector: Did you close the window after you?

Watchman: No, I left it open.

Inspector: What did you do after that?

Watchman: I made my way with some difficulty to the library.

Inspector: Was it then that you telephoned headquarters?

Watchman: Yes.

Inspector: How did you know where the telephone was?

Watchman: As soon as I opened the library door and turned on the light, I saw it.

Inspector: How did you tear the pocket of your coat?

Watchman: I tore it climbing in the window.

Inspector: And you say you saw no one leave the house?

Watchman: No sir.

Inspector: What reason do you think Mr. Parker had for committing suicide?

Watchman: I am sure I don't know.

Because of an inconsistency in the watchman's answers, the inspector held him on suspicion. *What was this inconsistency?*

Answer on page 131

COUNT THE TRAINS

CAN YOU ANSWER TOM'S QUESTION?

Answer on page 132

SUBURBS

Five members of a club are named Surbiton, Ealing, Tottenham, Richmond, and Blackheath. Each of them, curiously, lives in a suburb which is a namesake of one of the others. Each of them, moreover, *works* in a second suburb which is also a namesake of one of the others. No two of them either live or work in the same suburb.

The gentleman who lives at Surbiton works at Richmond.

Mr. Richmond works at Blackheath.

The Blackheath resident works in the suburb which is the namesake of the Surbiton resident.

Mr. Ealing works in the suburb which is the namesake of the Blackheath resident.

Who works at Ealing?

Answer on page 132

THE FIVE PEDAGOGUES

Dr. Mortarboard engages five instructors for his school: Mr. Botany, Mr. Geometry, Mr. French, Mr. History, and Mr. Syntax. Each is required to teach two of the subjects which correspond to their five names. No instructor, however, teaches the subject corresponding to his own name.

Mr. History plays cut-throat bridge with the two botany instructors.

Mr. Syntax is married to the sister of one geometry instructor, while his own sister is married to the other.

Mr. Botany knows no French, and Mr. French has no interest in syntax.

Mr. Geometry spends his holidays with the two history instructors.

Mr. History and Mr. Syntax share in the teaching of one subject.

French is not taught by the namesake of either subject taught by Mr. French.

All lessons in French and geometry take place at the same time.

What are the two subjects which the five pedagogues respectively teach?

Answer on page 132

THE STEEL BEAM

A steel beam balances on a scale with three-quarters of a beam and a ¾-pound weight. *How much does the beam weigh?*

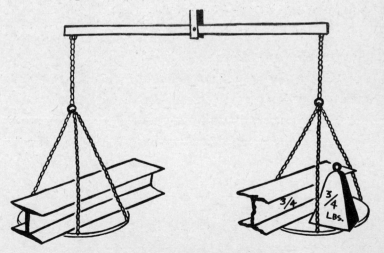

Answer on page 133

JUGGLING JUGS

Two merchants in partnership have purchased an eight-quart jug of olive oil. They want to divide the oil into two equal parts. However, all they have on hand for purposes of measuring are two jugs—one of which holds five quarts, and the other three quarts.

At first it seems impossible to effect an even division of four quarts each by using the three containers on hand; but they finally manage to do it. *Can you?*

Answer on page 133

THE SMALL GAME HUNTERS

HOW MANY QUAIL DID GERALD SHOOT?

Answer on page 134

THE FRATERNITY
CONVENTION

It is the last day of the 1966 Convention of the She Delta Deck Fraternity held at St. Louis. The Convention has been in session for a full week. Friends and acquaintances mingle in the lounge, smoking and chatting. Six of the members of the Fraternity, peculiarly enough, bear the names of certain professions or trades. It is these six men with which this particular problem is concerned. Significant bits of their conversation are here recorded.

Mr. Grocer has been asked by Mr. Butcher to join him during the week in a round of golf. Mr. Grocer regrets he cannot accept.

Mr. Butcher replies, "How silly of me! You couldn't play golf now, anyhow. You told me you mashed your finger at your store under a tub of butter. Let me see it."

Mr. Doctor and Mr. Artist render the following colloquy:

Mr. Doctor: I go deep-sea fishing with the lawyer each weekend.

Mr. Artist: The doctor, the grocer, and I live in Milwaukee.

Mr. Baker has buttonholed Mr. Lawyer.

Mr. Baker: I got in a new and interesting case at the office. I'll drop in and tell you about it some time next week.

PROBLEM: Assume that none of these six men bears the name of his business or profession and assume that no two of these men are in the same business or profession, and further assume that one is a lawyer, one is a grocer, one is a doctor, one is an artist, one is a baker, and one is a butcher—

Who is the lawyer?
Who is the grocer?
Who is the artist?
Who is the baker?
Who is the butcher?
Who is the doctor?

Answer on page 134

THE CHECKERBOARD

**WHAT IS THE SOLUTION TO THE
CHECKER PLAYER'S PROBLEM?**

Answer on page 136

DIRTY FACES

Two schoolboys were playing on the toolshed roof. Something gave way, and they were precipitated through the roof to the floor below.

When they picked themselves up, the face of one boy was covered with grime. The other boy's face was quite clean. Yet it was the boy with the clean face who at once went off and washed.

How is this to be explained?

Answer on page 137

THE PENSIONER

A pensioner remembered that he was sent to school when he was four-and-a-half years of age, and that he stayed at that same school for one-sixth of his life. Then he remained in the army for one-fifth of his life, and when he left the army he spent one-quarter of his life as a clerk. At present he had already spent one-third of his life in retirement. *What was the pensioner's age?*

Answer on page 137

THE CAT IN THE WELL

Through some misadventure, a cat fell down a well. The well was 18 feet deep. The cat managed to climb out, but only after experiencing great difficulty, since the sides of the well were damp and slippery.

For every minute of effort, the cat gained three feet. It was then too tired to struggle further and rested. During that next minute of rest, the cat slid back two feet.

How long did it take the cat to get out of the well?

Answer on page 137

A SQUARE IN LINDLAND

Blotto Square is a tiny square in Lindland. There is only one house on each of its four sides. These sides may be called the north side, east side, south side, and west side.

The residents of the four houses are Mr. East, Mr. West, Mr. North, and Mr. South. They are (not necessarily respectively) a lawyer, a doctor, a sculptor, and an actor.

The resident on the north side of the square knows nothing about the law.

The doctor lives opposite Mr. South; the actor, opposite Mr. North.

The resident on the west side of the square has never passed an examination.

Mr. South, who has never been inside a theater, has enlisted the aid of the lawyer in an action now pending in the courts.

Mr. West is the actor's right-hand neighbor.

Draw a plan of Blotto Square showing each resident's house and occupation.

Answer on page 137

THE DRY GOODS DEALER

A dry goods dealer has a five-yard piece of 36-inch wide material. A lady wishes to purchase one and one-half yards. Neither a yardstick nor a tape measure, nor any other measuring device is available. *How is the difficulty solved?*

Answer on page 138

THE ROPE LADDER

HOW MANY LADDER RUNGS WILL BE
SUBMERGED TWO HOURS LATER?

Answer on page 138

THE TEACHER'S DILEMMA

A teacher is trying to figure out how many students he can put in the classroom without having more than two students in any one row, including all the diagonal rows.

Can you help him out? Two students have already been seated, so no more students are permitted in that corner-to-corner diagonal.

Answer on page 138

THE SIX AUTHORS

Six authors are seated three on a side in a first-class railway compartment. Their names are Black, Brown, Gray, Green, Pink, and White. They are (but not respectively) an essayist, an historian, a humorist, a novelist, a playwright, and a poet.

Each has written a book which one or the other occupants of the compartment is reading.

Mr. Black is reading essays.

Mr. Gray is reading a book by the author sitting opposite to him.

Mr. Brown is sitting between the essayist and the humorist.

Mr. Pink is sitting next to the playwright.

The essayist is facing the historian.

Mr. Green is reading plays.

Mr. Brown is the novelist's brother-in-law.

Mr. Black, who is in a corner seat, has no interest in history.

Mr. Green is facing the novelist.

Mr. Pink is reading a book by the humorist.

Mr. White never reads poetry.

Identify each of the six authors.

Answer on page 138

THE DIFFICULT CROSSING

A farmer must transport a dog, a duck, and a bag of corn from one side of a river to the opposite bank. The craft he is using is very small—only large enough for him to take one of his possessions at any one time. If he leaves the dog alone with the duck, the dog is likely to make short work of the duck. If he leaves the duck alone with the corn, the duck will make short work of the corn.

What is the least number of trips the farmer can take to manage safely?

Answer on page 139

THE FOUR GOATS

A farmer has four goats tethered one at each corner of a square field 100 feet by 100 feet. The tethers are of such a length that each goat can graze over a sector of 50 feet radius. The goats therefore are compelled to leave uneaten a portion in the center of the field.

Three of the goats are sold, and the farmer lengthens the tether of the remaining goat. He finds that he has made the rope just long enough to allow the goat to graze over an area equal to the combined area the four goats had previously grazed over. *What was the length of the tether?*

Answer on page 139

THE DARING YOUNG MAN

HOW DOES THE YOUNG MAN
CROSS THE BRIDGE SAFELY?

Answer on page 139

THE COUNTERFEIT COIN

A king of ancient days once wished to reward one of his wise men, so he had his servants lay before the sage nine coins and a balance scale.

Addressing the object of his largesse, the king said, "There are nine coins here. Eight of them are made of pure gold. One of them has been debased by a lesser metal, which of course, does not weigh as much as gold.

"Now," continued the king, "you will determine your own reward. If you weigh each coin separately, you will, of course, find out which coin weighs the least, and that one will obviously be the counterfeit coin. But if you proceed in that manner you will be obliged to use the balance scale nine times. You would then achieve the worst result, for every time you use the scale, you lose one coin. You can take 15 minutes to think over how to proceed. Since you are a very wise man, you will manage to use the balance scale the fewest possible number of times."

The sage retired for a few minutes, and then came back and addressed himself to the king. "Sire," he said, "I am now ready to pick the counterfeit coin." And he proceeded to do this, using the scale the least number of times necessary to determine which of the nine coins was the counterfeit.

How did he contrive to find out? How many times did he use the scale?

Answer on page 139

THE PROBLEM
OF THE CHAINS

A mechanic has six pieces of chain, each containing five links. He wants to make a continuous piece of 30 links.

It costs 20 cents to cut a link open, and it costs 50 cents to weld the opening back again. A new continuous chain, all in one piece, can be bought for $4. *How much can be saved if the chain is put together in the most economical manner?*

Answer on page 140

THE OHIO LIMITED

The Ohio Limited is controlled by an engineer, a fireman, and a guard, whose names are Brown, Jones, and Robinson, *not* respectively.

On the train are three passengers: Mr. Jones, Mr. Robinson, and Mr. Brown.

Mr. Robinson lives in Cleveland.

The guard lives halfway between Cleveland and New York.

Mr. Jones's income is $9,120.11 per year.

The guard earns in a year exactly one-third of the income of his nearest neighbor, who is a passenger.

The guard's namesake lives in New York.

Brown beat the fireman at billiards.

What is the name of the engineer?

Answer on page 140

THE STMIED SAVAGE

WHAT DID THE MISSIONARY SAY?

Answer on page 140

NARROW ESCAPE

Mr. Drake was driving his car along a straight highway in Florida, which led due north to his destination, a town 20 miles north of his starting point. When he had gone approximately 19 miles, a fast-moving car passed his. As a result his car was forced a couple of yards off the highway, thereby scraping its side against some protruding bushes.

Drake stopped his car, and as he was looking out the window to ascertain whether any noticeable damage had been done by the bushes, he judged from the position of the sun that it was late in the afternoon and that he would have to hurry. A couple of minutes later he arrived at his destination, happy in the thought that he had escaped a possible serious accident.

What is the fallacy in the above story?

Answer on page 141

THE SAHARA EXPEDITION

Charles Wayne Looksee, noted African explorer, is preparing to fulfill his life's ambition—to chart the trackless sands of the Sahara. A trip straight across the desert would be hazardous enough, but Looksee's journey will be doubly dangerous, since he must travel a roundabout route so as to make observations.

One of Looksee's biggest problems is equipment. For the automobile, he buys special heat-resistant tires, each of which is guaranteed to last 12,000 miles. It is extremely important that he does not load his car with any more weight than is necessary, so he determines to rely completely on the guarantee. Now the problem is: *what is the least number of tires the explorer must buy to carry him through the 27,000-mile journey? And why?*

Answer on page 141

TRACKS IN THE SNOW

WHAT CAUSED THE TRACKS IN THE SNOW?

Answer on page 141

THE RAILROAD SIDING

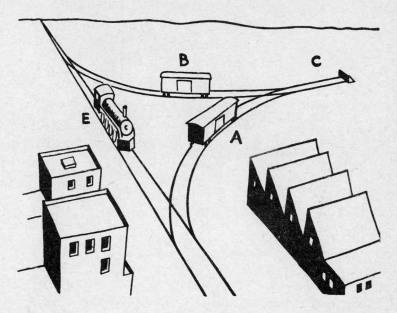

E is an engine on the main line. A and B are boxcars on the two sidings. The segment C is long enough to contain only one boxcar or the engine.

You are required, by means of the engine, to move B to A and A to B and to leave E in its original position. *How would you do it?*

Answer on page 142

THE CLEVER BLIND MAN

Three men are seated around a circular table facing each other. They are told that a box in the room contains five hats—three white and two black. A hat is placed on each man's head. The remaining two hats are unseen. No man sees the hat that is placed on his own head.

One man is then asked what color hat he believes to be on his head. He looks at the other two hats before him on the heads of his companions, and then says he doesn't know.

The second man in reply to a similar question admits that he too, doesn't really know.

The question is then put once again, and the

third man, *who is blind*, correctly announces the color of the hat on his head.

Can you tell what color that hat was and can you outline the reasoning which the blind man followed?

Answer on page 142

THE CHESS TOURNAMENT

Four men named P. F. Smith, C. J. Smith, Reynolds, and Fellows played in a chess tournament.

The Smiths were the famous Smith twins who starred on the Princeton football team.

Reynolds surprised everyone when he defeated Fellows.

The man who finished third said graciously to the winner at the conclusion of the matches, "I've heard a great deal about you and I am happy to meet you. May I congratulate you."

The runner-up had been terribly crippled since he was four years old. As a result he had never married, but had lived a sheltered life with his widowed mother, making chess his chief diversion.

P. F. Smith sometimes drank too much. He had disgraced himself when he was an usher at Fellow's wedding by proposing to the bride's mother.

In what order did the men finish?

Answer on page 143

THE CLIMBING MONKEY

A rope is passed over a frictionless pulley, which is suspended from the ceiling. From one end of the rope there is suspended a 15-pound weight that exactly balances a monkey who is holding on to the other end of the rope.

If the monkey climbs the rope, will he rise above or sink below the height of the weight?

Answer on page 143

THE SWISS MILKMAIDS

WHICH GIRL HAS THE HEAVIEST MILK CAN?

WHICH THE LIGHTEST?

Answer on page 144

FATHEAD'S FARM

Life is very difficult on Fathead's farm. He employs a ploughman, a carter, a shepherd, and a driver. And their names, as it happens, are Ploughman, Carter, Shepherd, and Driver. It would be very convenient if each of them had the name corresponding to his vocation, but unfortunately none of them has.

But that's not all. Each of these four has a son who assists one of the others. None of them, that is, assists his own father. Nor does any of them work with the fellow whose calling is the same as his own name.

The following facts are known:

Young Ploughman is engaged to the sister of the young fellow who helps the carter.

The carter is married to Mr. Ploughman's sister.

Mr. Shepherd is married to the ploughman's widowed mother.

Mr. Driver has no daughter.

What are the vocations of each of Fathead's employees, and whom do their respective sons assist?

Answer on page 144

THE LILY POND

A certain pond in Central America is a perfect circle twenty feet in diameter. Every year a magnificent water-lily appears in the exact center of the pond. The lily grows with remarkable rapidity, doubling its area every day; at the end of exactly twenty-one days, the lily fills the entire area of the pond. Then it dies away and for twelve months no more is seen of it.

At the end of how many days from its first appearance does the lily occupy half the area of the pond?

Answer on page 144

THE BLIND BUTLER

WHAT IS THE LEAST NUMBER OF
SOCKS HE MUST BRING BACK?

Answer on page 145

THE VICTORY COLUMN

In a public square stands a column commemorating a great victory. The shaft of the column is 200 feet high and 30 feet in circumference.

The shaft is wreathed in a spiral garland which passes around the shaft exactly five times.

What is the length of the garland?

Answer on page 145

THE RIDDLE
OF THE RED WINE

Two friars, Brother Boniface and the abbot, are seated at a table, upon which rests a pint jug of water and a pint bottle of red wine. The abbot pours a glass of wine and empties it into the jug of water. Then he fills a glass from the water jug and empties it into the bottle of wine.

"Tell me, Brother Boniface," the abbot demands, "have I taken more wine from the bottle than water from the jug? Or have I taken more water from the jug than wine from the bottle?"

Can you answer the abbot's question?

Answer on page 145

THE VANISHED COIN

The eight members of an exclusive society in London known as the Collector's Club are each considered experts and connoisseurs of objets d'art, stamps, and coins.

The Club does not admit outsiders to its meetings, and even bars waiters from serving the bowls of fruit which invariably grace the long table at which the informal, fortnightly discussions are held.

One day one of the members met an acquaintance who also was a collector of coins. The friend, who had heard much about the famed discussions at the Club, was so insistent about being taken to a meeting that the member, succumbing to his friend's entreaties, obtained permission to have him attend.

During the meeting, Mr. Grant Lewis, a coin collector, just returned from a Continental tour, exhibited his prize find—an ancient, rare Phoenician coin. The coin passed from hand to hand and was closely scrutinized by all those present, amidst a continual barrage of questions directed at the proud Lewis. Lewis, urged to expatiate on the history of his rarity, surrendered to the importunities of his fellow members. He requested the silver piece in order to point out certain peculiarities; but no one had the coin.

Each averred he had passed it to another, so that from the maze of statements it was impossible to determine who actually had the coin last. Every inch of

the carpet was examined, but the coin seemed to have vanished into thin air. Everyone volubly urged calm, thus indicating how upset the members actually were. Fear lest the scandal besmirch the honor of the venerable Collector's Club crowded out the suspicion that perhaps a hoax was being perpetrated, for the coin was worth a fabulous sum.

Finally, the demand was made that everyone submit to a personal examination. The suggestion was taken up and seconded with willingness by all—that is, all except the stranger. He demurred resolutely. Not only would he not submit to a search of his person, but he steadfastly refused to divulge any reason for his apparently stubborn refusal. The chairman threatened to inform the police. As the words fell from his lips, Grant Lewis reached forth nervously into the silver bowl for an apple. As he drew the fruit away, there to his amazement, at the bottom of the bowl, he saw his prize coin. Confusion succeeded bewilderment; and profuse apologies poured forth upon the stranger, who rose to explain.

The explanation for his refusing to be searched and refusing further to give a reason for his attitude was sound. All the facts necessary for a logical explanation of the stranger's actions are in the foregoing recital. *What sensible and logical explanation did the stranger offer?*

Answer on page 146

THE EGG MAN

An egg man sold to Mr. Jones half his stock of eggs and half an egg. He then sold to Smith half of his remaining stock and half an egg. Then Robinson bought half of the eggs which he had left and half an egg. Finally Brown bought the rest of his stock, namely 33 eggs.

How many eggs did the egg man have to start with? He did not sell any broken eggs!

Answer on page 146

THE STOLEN NECKLACE

WHICH MAN IS TELLING THE WHOLE TRUTH?

Answer on page 146

THE FOOTBALL TOURNAMENT

An elimination tournament in football was held in which four colleges—Trinity, Tufts, Temple, and Tulane—participated. The winners of the first two games met in the third and final game to decide the championship. The colors of the various teams were brown, blue, red, and purple, and the competing captains were Albie, Barry, Bill, and Ben, though not necessarily respectively. The following facts are known:

(1) In the final game Albie's team made its only score by a touchdown on the first play, but missed the point after touchdown.

(2) The red team lost to Tufts in the first game.

(3) Ben's team defeated Tulane 12 to 0.

(4) The captain of the purple team saved his team from being scoreless in the third game by a 40-yard field goal.

(5) Ben's team did not play Trinity.

(6) Barry's team lost to the undefeated team.

(7) Albie did not see his former friend, the captain of the brown team.

Who defeated whom in the play-off, and by what score?

Who was the captain of each team?

What was the color of each team?

Answer on page 147

THE MUNICIPAL RAILWAYS

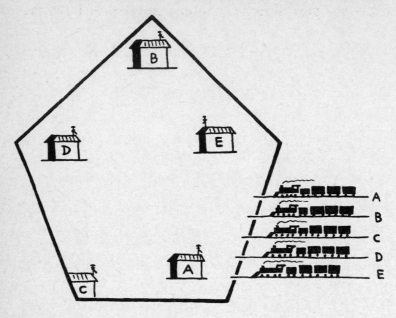

The illustration shows the plan of a city surrounded by pentagonal fortifications. Five railroad companies are clamoring for a concession to run a railway into the city. After deliberating, the mayor announces, "Let every one of them have a concession—but the line of one company must never cross the line of another!"

The letters in the diagram represent five railroad companies, and indicate just where each line must enter the city, and where the terminal belonging to that line must be located.

Trace out the route for the line A to A, B to B,

C to C, and so on, so that one line does not cross another, or pass through another company's terminal.

Answer on page 148

THE SIMPLE-MINDED MAID

A gentleman picked up the telephone just as his maid answered a call on another extension. The conversation he listened in on went as follows:

"Is Mr. Smith at home?"

"I will ask him, sir. What name shall I give him?

"Quoit."

"What's that, sir?"

"Quoit."

"Would you mind spelling it?"

"*Q* for quick, *U* for umbrella, *O* for omnibus, *I* for idiot—"

"*I* for what, sir?"

"*I* for idiot, *T* for telephone. *Q, U, O, I, T*, Quoit."

"Thank you, sir."

The gentleman remarked to himself that his maid could not be too intelligent. *Why?*

Answer on page 149

THE BLIND ABBOT

An old medieval tale tells of a blind abbot who had 20 prodigal monks under his care. He and his charges lived in the top story of a square tower which was arranged in nine cells as illustrated. He himself occupied the center cell.

Each night it was his habit to patrol the abbey and to count his charges in order to make sure that the monks were all at home. His own peculiar method of tallying was to count nine heads for each wall. If he got a full count, he took it for granted that all were present.

Now a certain sly fellow arranged the beds so that two of the boys could leave of a night and make whoopee without the old codger suspecting any A.W.O.L.

On another night, this shrewd young fellow even

contrived to bring in four comrades from a neighboring monastery for a party. He arranged the group so cleverly that when the abbot made his evening round, he still counted only nine heads along each wall.

A few months later, the boys decided to give a grand blow-out. They increased the attendance to 32, but still the abbot did not sense that anything was amiss.

And as a grand finale, they held one big gala super-affair, at which 36 monks attended, but still the blind abbot counted but nine heads along each wall.

Now the problem is to discover how that wily brother arranged the monks in each cell so that 18, 20, 24, 32, and 36 friars were present, although the blind abbot in each case counted nine heads along each wall of the tower.

Answer on page 149

	BLIND ABBOT'S CELL	

NAME THE CARDS

CAN YOU NAME THE THREE CARDS?

Answer on page 150

THE STOLEN CAMEO

Sir Michael Farnsworth was elated. From some tumbledown shop in Leghorn he had brought back to England a cameo which he knew was a premier specimen. He presented his find for appraisal to Geoffrey Warren, senior member of Warren & Co., dealers in objets d'art for more than two hundred years. Mr. Warren, after careful scrutiny, acclaimed the carved piece a veritable masterpiece.

Sir Michael determined to deed the cameo to the British Museum.

Four days later, Sir Michael again appeared at Warren's. His gift had been accepted. The cameo wanted furbishing. Geoffrey Warren stated that he himself would attend to the matter, for he would not entrust so precious a piece to any but his own practiced hands. The same afternoon, a reporter from *The Times* obtained a statement from Mr. Warren. The old gentleman, departing from the conservatism of years, pronounced the Farnsworth cameo to be the finest specimen extant.

Two days later, Scotland Yard was notified that the solid house of Warren and Company had been despoiled of its greatest treasure. The Farnsworth cameo had been stolen. The police, after routine examination and routine questioning, rendered their routine report. Sir Michael was told that the house of

Warren and Company would stand by its loss. The cameo was worth £5,000—£5,000 would be paid.

But Sir Michael was shocked far beyond the thought of money. He had been robbed of fame. Secretly he engaged one of the most brilliant private detectives in London. Within three hours he was informed that Geoffrey Warren himself had stolen the cameo.

At first Sir Michael wouldn't believe it. The thought was preposterous. The man had been entrusted with millions during his long, honorable career. Furthermore, the cameo, publicized throughout the world of art, was the only one of its kind and could never be resold. A collector, though he were in Tibet, would recognize it immediately. As to the idea that Geoffrey Warren had purloined the precious cameo simply for the joy of possession, that too was absurd. Had not Geoffrey Warren held within the palm of his hand for more than forty years the finest gems that existed? However, confronted with the accusation, Geoffrey Warren readily confessed.

The problem is to determine what motive impelled Mr. Warren to the theft of the cameo. The answer is not to be found in some extraneous circumstance, such as a personal grievance. A broad hint to the solution will be found in the fact that after the theft was discovered, Farnsworth and Warren remained good friends.

Answer on page 150

THE MURDERED
CARD PLAYER

Four men, whom we shall call Robert, Ronald, Ralph and Rudolph, were playing cards one evening. As a result of a quarrel during the course of the game, one of these men shot and killed another. From the facts given below, see if you can determine who the murderer and his victim were.

Robert will not expose his brother's guilt.

Rudolph had been released from jail on the day of the murder, after having served a three-day sentence.

Robert had wheeled Ralph, a cripple, to the card game at Ronald's house.

Rudolph had known Ronald for only five days before the murder.

Ralph had met Robert's father only once.

The host is about to give evidence against the murderer, whom he dislikes.

The murdered man had eaten dinner on the previous night with one of the men who did not customarily bowl with Ronald.

Answer on page 150

THE HANGING SCALES

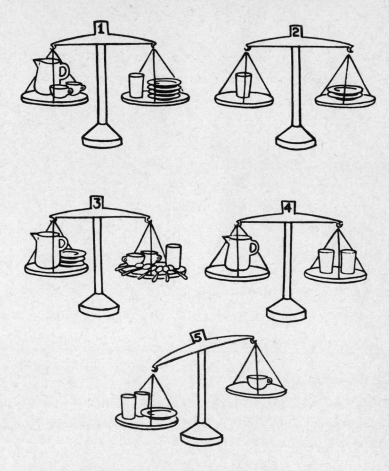

**HOW MANY SPOONS MUST BE ADDED TO THE
RIGHT SIDE OF SCALE FIVE TO MAKE IT BALANCE?**

Answer on page 151

THE FRUIT PEDDLERS

Three fruit peddlers stood beside their pushcarts hawking their wares. They were each selling apples and each pushcart carried an identical price sign. The signs were the kind which are generally used by fruit peddlers. Similar signs may be seen every weekday in every marketplace in the land.

The first peddler had fifteen apples to sell; he sold them all.

The second peddler had fourteen apples to sell; he sold them all.

The third peddler had thirteen apples to sell; he sold them all.

At the end of the day, they found that each had realized exactly the same amount of money for his apples.

The apples were not sold by weight or by measure. None of the apples was rotten; none of the apples was given away; none of the peddlers ate any of his apples; nor was any peddler given counterfeit money.

How do you account for the strange results?

Answer on page 151

MRS. ADDEM'S CHILDREN

Mrs. Addem's age is three times the sum of the ages (in years) of her children.

This ratio will, of course, decrease from year to year. In 11 years' time Mrs. Addem's age will equal the sum of her children's ages.

The age (in years) of the eldest child is equal to the product of the ages of the other two.

No two children were born in the same year.

What are the children's ages?

Answer on page 152

FIGHT TO THE FINISH

WHICH BOXER IS RELATED TO TIM?

WHAT IS THE RELATIONSHIP?

Answer on page 152

THE SCHOLARSHIP EXAMINATION

Five boys sat for a scholarship examination. In each of five subjects—Latin, English, science, mathematics, and history—60 marks were divided among the five boys. Each boy was awarded at least one mark in each subject. Each boy, curiously enough, was first in one subject, second in another, third in another, fourth in another, and fifth in yet another. Their aggregate marks, however, differed. The scholarship award was based on aggregate marks.

The following facts were reported:

Alfred took third place in Latin. In English, however, he scored 27 marks against David's 26.

Bertram scored 12 marks in science and was bottom but one in mathematics, scoring only 2.

Cyril was bottom in history, with 10 marks.

David, with 18 marks, took third place in mathematics.

Egbert took top place in history, but was bottom in science, with only 9 marks.

The top mark in Latin was 14.

Who won the scholarship, and what were the aggregate marks of the winner and his rivals?

Answer on page 153

THE SIX HOODLUMS

Serena Vashti Malloy, a rich dowager, was found murdered in her home in Chicago with a bullet through her heart. The local police ascertained that the murder was committed between 10 and 12 o'clock at night, and that the motive was robbery. They were also sure that the crime was committed by one of a notorious gang of local criminals.

They rounded up the gang, and at the preliminary arraignment each of the six suspects was questioned. Each of the men made two significant statements. In each case, one of the statements was true, and one of the statements was false. (The order of the statements as presented is not controlling.)

The judge, aware of this state of affairs, deliberated awhile and soon became rightfully convinced of the guilt of one of the men in particular. *Which one did he accuse?*

The statements follow:

Mike: Red didn't kill her. I never saw a gun in my life.

Dan: I was in Philly when it happened. Mat did it.

Jim: Mike pulled the trigger. All of us except Dan were in Chi when it happened.

Spud: Only one of us witnessed the murder. I was not even in town on the night of the killing.

Mat: Spud's the murderer. I was at the neighborhood movies, at the time, with some other one of the boys.

Red: Me and Mike were together from 10 to 12 away from the rest of the gang. Dan killed her.

Answer on page 153

SMOKE GETS IN YOUR EYES

HOW MANY CIGARETTES CAN
THEY MAKE FROM THE BUTTS?

Answer on page 155

THREE SONS

Smith, Sr., Brown, Sr., and Jones, Sr., each had a grown son. We may call the sons Smith, Jr., Brown, Jr., and Jones, Jr. One of the Juniors was a politician; another, a banker; and the third, a lawyer.

(1) The lawyer frequently played tennis with his father.

(2) Brown, Jr., called the politician a socialist.

(3) The politician's father played golf every Wednesday with another of the older men.

(4) Smith, Sr., had been a paralytic from youth. *What was the name of the lawyer?*

Answer on page 156

THE FIVE OFFICE BOYS

Five office boys were examined by their employer in reading, writing, arithmetic, geography, and history. The marking system was simple: 10 marks in all were awarded in each subject and divided among the boys.

When the examination was over, the results were announced in the following roundabout way:

The order of merit in the examination as a whole is: (1) Percy; (2) Walter; (3) Fred; (4) Cyril; (5) Foch. Each boy was tops in one subject. No two boys, in any one subject, were given the same mark.

Foch was tops in history; Walter in geography.

Fred was tops in reading. He received the same mark in writing as in arithmetic and the same mark in geography as in history.

Cyril was tops in writing and third in arithmetic.

In reading, Foch was second and Percy third.

Walter was not bottom in anything. In two subjects, Walter did better than Percy.

Foch gained as many marks in one subject as in the other four put together.

Draw up a table showing each boy's mark in each subject.

Answer on page 156

A CASE OF ORANGES

Four women—Mary, Jane, Kate, and Eliza—chipped in and bought a case containing 233 oranges. They divided them up in proportion to the amount of money each woman chipped in.

Mary received 20 more oranges than Jane, 53 more than Kate, and 71 more than Eliza.

How many oranges did each woman receive?

Answer on page 156

IT REALLY
HAPPENED ONE NIGHT

A charming hedonist, whom we'll call Winston, came home one night at about 2 A.M., rather tired after the revels of the night. He went to bed directly. About twenty minutes later, he got up, opened the local telephone book, and looked up the number of one Gerald Malcolm. He called, and a sweet soprano answered.

"Hello! Is this Mrs. Malcolm?" queried Winston.

"Yes."

"I would like to speak to Mr. Malcolm."

"He's asleep."

"But it's very important!" Winston insisted.

"Important! Well, hold the wire a moment and I'll awaken him."

Young Winston glued his ear to the receiver long enough to hear Mrs. Malcolm walking off spouseward. *Then he deliberately hung up!*

Now ruling out any hoax or wager, and hypothecating that Winston had never previously met or communicated with either Mr. or Mrs. Malcolm, and assuming that Winston acted premeditatedly and planned *everything* he did, *what motive can you assign for his action?*

Answer on page 157

BOOTS

Mr. Cobblewell, a bootmaker, sold a pair of boots to a well-dressed stranger, who tendered a $50 bill in payment. As he had no change, Mr. Cobblewell went next door and had his friend Plaster, the druggist, change the bill. The price of the boots was $46. The stranger took his change and left.

Shortly afterwards Plaster appeared in Cobblewell's shop in a state of much agitation to explain that the $50 bill he had been given was counterfeit. Naturally, Cobblewell had no option but to replace it with a good $50 bill.

How much has Cobblewell lost?

Answer on page 157

THE LOST COIN

WHO IS ENTITLED TO THE COIN?

Answer on page 157

THE CARETAKER

Adam Smith was caretaker of an unoccupied old mansion from which all of the furniture had been removed, with the exception of the few pieces that graced the little back room in which Smith lived the life of a recluse. His only known contacts were with the little corner store and with the milk man, whom he paid each week. This person, upon finding that several bottles of milk were still standing on the stairs as he had left them and that there was no response to repeated knockings on the door, summoned the police. They entered the house and found the body of Smith hanging by the neck from the lofty chandelier in the center of the dusty and vacant ballroom.

It was a weird sight in the semi-darkness to see the limp figure of the man dangling in the empty center of what had once been a brilliant and beautiful salon. The police and the coroner, who had subsequently been called, cut down the body and made an examination. The man was suspended by his own belt and there was nothing further that they could observe except two cigarette stubs and an empty whisky flask on the floor, and the dust and cobwebs that covered the high ceiling and the barren walls.

Glad to be through with his unpleasant task, the coroner made the death certificate and assigned as cause of death "Suicide due to melancholia."

What was the fallacy in the coroner's explanation?

Answer on page 158

THE STOLEN ANTIQUE

Three men—Mr. White, Mr. Black, Mr. Brown—and their wives were entertained at the home of a friend one evening. After the departure of the guests, the host and the hostess discovered that a valuable antique had been stolen. It later developed that one of the six guests was the thief.

It is known that:

The spouse of the thief lost money at cards that evening.

Because of partial paralysis of his hands and arms, Mr. Brown was unable to drive his car.

Mrs. Black and another female guest spent the entire evening doing a jig-saw puzzle.

Mr. Black accidentally spilled a drink on Mrs. White when he was introduced to her.

Mr. Brown gave his wife half of the money he had won to make up for her loss.

Mr. Black had beaten the thief in golf that day.

Who was the thief?

Answer on page 158

THE MAILBOX

Mr. Contango, a London businessman, went to Paris for a month's holiday. He gave Miss Smith, his secretary, the key to his office, asking her to carry on while he was away, and also to forward all letters. However, he omitted to give her the key to the mailbox.

At the end of some days, he rang up Miss Smith and inquired why he had received no letters. She explained that he had not left her the key. Mr Contango promised to forward it at once.

The key was duly posted, but still no letters came for Mr. Contango. On returning home, therefore, he promptly sacked his secretary.

Was he justified in doing so?

Answer on page 158

THE ADVENTUROUS SNAIL

Two philosophers were walking in a garden when one of them noticed a snail making the perilous ascent of a wall 20 feet high. Judging by the trail, the gentlemen calculated that the snail ascended three feet each day, sleeping and slipping back two feet each night.

"Pray tell me," said one philosopher to his companion, "how long will it take the snail to climb to the top of the wall and descend the other side. The top of the wall, as you know, has a sharp edge, so that when he gets there he will instantly begin to descend, putting precisely the same exertion into his daily climbing down as he did in his climbing up, and sleeping and slipping at night as before."

Can you figure out the answer? (Assume that the day is equally divided into 12 hours' daytime and 12 hours' night.)

Answer on page 159

THE FOUR COEDS

**WHAT IS THE ANSWER TO
PROFESSOR BROWN'S QUESTION?**

Answer on page 159

THE DEAD TOURIST

Mr. and Mrs. Samuel Elkins, wealthy society folks, went on a trip to Switzerland to enjoy some mountain climbing.

A few weeks later, the attractive Mrs. Elkins, shrouded in heavy black returned to her home in Boston, a widow. Mr. Elkins had missed his step while on a climbing expedition, and had been precipitated headlong down a glassy ravine to a horrible death at the base of the mountain. It was a terrible accident and a terrible ordeal for the stricken Mrs. Elkins, who was with him at the time and witnessed the tragedy.

About a month after her return, her friends, who had given her their deepest sympathy, were astounded to hear that she had been indicted for the murder of her husband. But they were more shocked when Mrs. Elkins broke down and confessed!

The police had received the tip-off from a certain Mr. Harper, head of a well-known travel agency. Mr. Harper had never left the United States.

How did he deduce that Mrs. Elkins had murdered her husband?

Answer on page 159

AN EXERCISE IN LOGIC

Assume that the following statement is true: "John is over twenty-one if John can vote."

Which of the following statements are then necessarily *true also?*

(1) If John cannot vote, John is not over twenty-one.

(2) If John is over twenty-one, he can vote.

(3) If John is not over twenty-one, he cannot vote.

(4) Either John can vote or John is not over twenty-one.

(5) Either John cannot vote or he is over twenty-one.

(6) Either John can vote or he is over twenty-one.

(7) Either John cannot vote or he is not over twenty-one.

Answer on page 159

THE ISLAND OF KO

On the island of Ko there are three types of inhabitants, physically indistinguishable from one another. They are known as the Reds, the Greens, and the Half-Breeds. A Red, when asked a question, invariably gives a truthful answer; a Green invariably gives an untruthful answer; a Half-Breed alternately lies and tells the truth, though one cannot tell whether his first answer will be a truthful one or not.

Three inhabitants—a Red, a Green, and a Half-Breed—were lounging on the beach. Their names (not necessarily respectively) were Tom, Dick, and Harry. A traveler accosted the first one and the following dialogue ensued:

"What is your name?"

"Tom, sir."

"Are you a Red, a Green, or a Half-Breed?"

"Green, sir."

"What is the name of your Red friend?"

"Dick, sir."

What are the names of the Red, the Green, and the Half-Breed?

Answer on page 160

THE ESCAPING PRISONER

A convict escapes from prison and has a half hour's start on two guards and a bloodhound who race after him. The guards' speed in four miles per hour; the dog's speed is 12 miles per hour; but the prisoner can do only three miles per hour. The dog runs up to the prisoner and then back to the guards, and so on back and forth until the guards catch the prisoner.

How far does the dog travel altogether?

Answer on page 160

THE TWO STUDENTS

HOW DO YOU ACCOUNT FOR THE FACT
THAT THE BOYS ARE NOT TWINS?

Answer on page 160

FIVE MASTERS

"There's a prize," said Mrs. Prigg to her daughters, "for the girl who does best in a little test I've devised for you. These five postcards"—she arranged them on the piano—"are copies of paintings by Degas, Klee, Matisse, Picasso, and Renoir. Which is by whom? I've numbered the postcards from one to five. Here are pencil and paper. You will each make out a list, and the one who does best gets the prize."

Shortly afterwards Mrs. Prigg collected the lists. "You might have done worse," was her verdict, "but there must have been a lot of guesswork. No one gets the prize, however—all five of you have scored the same number of points."

The girls' lists were:

Kitty: (1) Renoir; (2) Matisse; (3) Picasso; (4) Degas; (5) Klee.

Beryl: (1) Matisse; (2) Picasso; (3) Renoir; (4) Degas; (5) Klee.

Lorna: (1) Degas; (2) Picasso; (3) Renoir; (4) Klee; (5) Matisse.

Doris: (1) Klee; (2) Matisse; (3) Degas; (4) Picasso; (5) Renoir.

May: (1) Degas; (2) Picasso; (3) Matisse; (4) Renoir; (5) Klee.

Assign the appropriate number to each artist.

Answer on page 160

THE ANSWERS

THE HONEY JARS . . . . Page 9

We know that each shelf contains 18 quarts of honey. If we remove the six smallest-sized jars from each of the two lower shelves, we are left with two big jars on the middle shelf and four medium jars on the lower shelf. Therefore, one big jar holds as much honey as two medium jars.

After replacing the small jars, we remove the two large jars from the middle shelf and their equivalent from the top shelf: one large jar and two medium ones. This leaves one medium and three small jars on the top shelf, and six small jars on the middle shelf, which shows that a medium jar holds as much as three small jars.

Thus, if we were to replace all the large jars with two medium ones, and then replace all the medium jars with three small ones, we would have 54 small jars. If 54 small jars hold 54 (3 x 18) quarts, then a small jar will hold one quart, a medium jar will hold three quarts, and a large jar will hold six quarts.

BEAR UP! . . . . Page 10

The white bear. Restating the problem, it seems that Sir Burton walked three miles due south, then five miles due east and that he was then only three miles away from where he first started. This would be possible only under one condition—if he had started walking from the North Pole.

It is not possible to go north of the North Pole—or east or west; you can only go south. If Sir Burton started walking from the North Pole and traveled three miles due south, then no matter how far he traveled due west or east, he was no further than three miles from the North Pole.

As the only kind of bear to be found in the region of the North Pole is the Polar Bear, which is white, then on the trip in question, Sir Burton must have brought back the white bearskin as a trophy.

KILLED IN ACTION . . . . Page 11

Young. Since Mrs. Lewis had never had a niece or nephew, and since Mrs. Smith had once had a daughter, Mrs. Smith could not have been the sister of Mrs. Lewis. Therefore, the slain man could not have been Mr. Smith.

Stacey returned alive to this country and hence is eliminated.

Because the slain man was married, Jones could not have been he.

It is obvious from statement (2) that the victim could not have been Lewis.

Therefore, by elimination, the slain man must have been Young.

APPOINTMENT IN ABILENE . . . . Page 12

Sixty miles. Let the distance from Poppon's home to Abilene be d and let the time it takes to travel distance d at 15 miles per hour be t. Then the time it takes to travel distance d at 10 miles per hour will be $t + 2$.

We now have two equations:

$$d = 15 \text{ mph} \times t$$
$$d = 10 \text{ mph} \times (t + 2)$$

Clearly, then:

$$15t = 10 (t + 2)$$
$$t = 4 \text{ hours}$$

Traveling four hours at 15 miles per hour, Poppon will cover 60 miles.

Astounding as it may be, half the foliage was gone no earlier than the thirtieth or last day. Since each day twice as many leaves were eaten as on the previous day, on the thirtieth day twice as many leaves were eaten as were consumed on the twenty-ninth day.

Now the total number of leaves eaten on the thirtieth day was greater by one than the total number of leaves consumed on the first 29 days. This can be demonstrated by merely accounting for (let us say) five days. On the first day, one leaf was eaten. On the second day, two. On the third day, four. On the fourth day, eight; and on the fifth day, 16. The total number of leaves eaten during the first four days equalled 15 leaves, while on the fifth day the number was 16, or one more than all the others combined.

This mathematical relationship will hold true no matter how many days are reckoned. There will always be one more in the last number than there will be found in the total of all the previous numbers combined.

The question is, when was half the foliage consumed. If we were dealing with only five days, 15½ leaves would constitute half of the total of 31 leaves. But since only a total of 15 leaves would be eaten in four days, we would have to wait until the fifth day to account for that extra half leaf which would bring the figure up to 50%. Similarly, in the given problem, half the foliage was not consumed until the thirtieth day.

THE MARKED FOREHEADS . . . . **Page 14**

Alex reasoned to himself as follows: Either the cross on my forehead is blue or it is green. I see a green cross on the forehead of Tom, and I see a green cross on the forehead of Joe. Each of us has his hand up because each of us sees at least one green cross. If my forehead were labeled with a blue cross, Joe would be putting his hand up solely because he sees a green cross on the forehead of Tom, while Tom would be putting his hand up solely because he sees a green cross on the forehead of Joe. But each one, seeing that my cross was a blue cross, would realize very soon that they were raising their hands because they saw a green cross on the forehead of each other. Being intelligent boys, either of them would have folded his arms by this time in the realization that his cross must have been marked green. For if the cross on Tom's forehead were blue, Tom would realize that Joe would not be raising his hand at all, and if the cross on Joe's forehead were blue, Joe would realize that Tom would not be raising his hand at all.

Therefore, it appears that both Tom and Joe are a bit confused and cannot make the foregoing deduction. The only reason that they cannot arrive at this conclusion must be that I am *not* marked with a blue cross.

THE FISHERMEN . . . . Page 15

Sixty-seven and one half pounds. When the two fishermen are balanced, the weight of one man multiplied by his distance from the fulcrum equals the weight of the second man multiplied by his distance from the fulcrum. Let these two distances be represented by x and y.

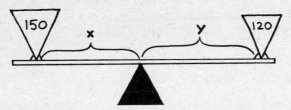

Then $150x = 120y$.

Let $x = 2$ (we need find only the proportion between the two distances, so for now we can let x be any number we choose). Then, $y = 2\frac{1}{2}$.

When the men switch places, the arrangement looks like this:

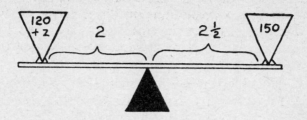

where z equals the weight of the fish.

$$(120 + z) \times 2 = 150 \times 2\frac{1}{2}.$$
$$z = 67\frac{1}{2} \text{ lbs.}$$

IN COLD BLOOD . . . . Page 16

The answer to this perplexing problem is to be found in the fact that it is a tenet of the law in all civilized countries that the innocent may not be made to suffer with the guilty. The sisters were Siamese twins.

THE CYCLISTS AND THE FLY . . . . Page 18

Fifteen miles. Since the riders are traveling at the same speed, they will meet exactly halfway between their starting points. They begin 20 miles apart; thus, they meet when each rider has traveled 10 miles.

Since they are traveling at the speed of 10 miles per hour, it will take each rider one hour to travel 10 miles. In one hour the fly, traveling at 15 miles per hour, will cover 15 miles, regardless of its path.

THE LEGIONNAIRES . . . . Page 19

Frank lives in Bangor; Tom lives in Miami; Sam lives in Los Angeles; John lives in Reno; Paul lives in Buffalo.

Frank says, "The state I come from borders on only

one other state." There is one state in the Union that borders on only one other state: the state of Maine. Therefore, Frank comes from Bangor.

Paul drove to the Convention in a car that has a license plate that begins with N. Only two of the four cities under consideration are in states beginning with the letter N. Therefore, Paul lives either in New York or Nevada. If we assume that Paul lives in Nevada, then Tom's statement, "I live west of Paul," becomes false because Reno is the farthest west of all five cities. It is therefore established that Paul lives in Buffalo.

Sam says, "I live east of John and north of Tom." Since Reno is farthest west, Sam must live in either Miami or Los Angeles. But Sam cannot live in Miami since that is the farthest city south, in which case he couldn't live north of anyone. Therefore, Sam lives in Los Angeles.

THE LADY AND THE TIGER . . . . Page 20

Before the waiting populace, he plunged his hand into the box, drew forth a paper, and then without reading it, plunged it into his mouth, chewed it, and swallowed it. He then calmly announced that the king's chamberlain would read the remaining piece of paper. Whatever word was written on the remaining piece of paper in the box, the one that he, the candidate, drew forth from the box was clearly the other alternative. Since the paper that was left had the word *Tiger* on it, it was clear to everybody that the young man had indeed won the princess.

THE FIRED WATCHMAN . . . . Page 22

Casey said that he had *dreamt* the night before that Peabody would be killed. Casey was the night watchman and must have been sleeping *on the job*.

THE STRANDED TEDDY BEAR . . . . Page 23

Father arranged the two planks as shown in the accompanying diagram. The shorter plank ran to the concrete island.

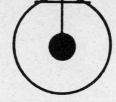

THE NOBLES AND THE SLAVES . . . . Page 24

Ugu and Tuga are nobles. Bugu is a slave. Tugu, whose answer Sir Wilfred did not hear, must have said, "I am a noble." If he were a slave he would lie and say that he was a noble. If he were a noble he would tell the truth and say, "I am a noble." Therefore, we can be sure that Ugu is telling the truth when he says, "Tugu says he is a noble." Therefore, the whole of his statement is true, and Ugu is also a noble. This automatically makes Bugu's statement false, proving that he is a slave.

AT CENTRAL STATION . . . . Page 25

Dan is going to Greenfields.

If he were going to Kemp, Midvale, or Deane, he would have purchased a $3 ticket. If he were going to Banstock, he would have gotten on the Midvale train. If he were bound for Fogwell, any train would do. So, Dan must be going to Greenfields.

DR. LIMEJUICE . . . . Page 26

Sniggersby held the lantern, and Wallop painted the doctor's nose.

Call the three boys A, B, and C (in order of interrogation), and their answers A1, A2, A3, and so on.

Then B3 and C3 are lies. Of the remaining statements two only are lies.

If B1 is a lie, A1 and C1 are both lies also; therefore B1 is true.

Then A1 or C1 must be true. It follows that A2 is true.

Now consider A1. If A1 is true, C1 is a lie. And since C3 is a lie, it follows that C is Wallop. In that case A3 is true as well as A1 and A2, which cannot be the case. Therefore A1 is a lie, and C1 is true.

Wallop cannot be A (for if he is, A1 and A3 are both lies) nor C (because C1 is true and if C is Wallop A3 is true also).

Therefore Wallop is B, and B2 is a lie.

Therefore Sniggersby held the lantern, and Wallop did the painting.

A is Sniggersby and C is Tittering.

RELATIVELY SIMPLE . . . . Page 28

Ann is Joan's daughter.

THE TWO CANOES . . . . Page 29

One thousand feet. When the two canoes meet at Point A (*see diagram*) they are 410 feet from one shore. The combined distance the two canoes have traveled is equal to the width of the river.

When they reach their destinations, the combined distance that they have traveled is equal to twice the width of the river.

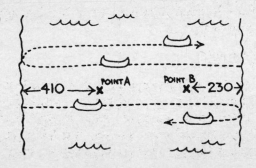

On the return trip, they meet at Point B. Now they have traveled a combined distance of three times the width of the river.

Since at the first meeting the two canoes had traveled a combined distance equal to the width of the river, at the second meeting each canoe has gone three times as far as it had gone when the two canoes first met.

At the first meeting, the slower canoe had gone 410 feet. When that paddler reaches Point B, he must have gone three times that distance, or 1,230 feet. As the diagram shows, this distance is 230 feet more than the width of the river. So we subtract 230 from 1,230 to find the width of the river, which is 1,000 feet.

The amount of time each canoe spends on shore between trips does not affect the problem.

THE HORSE RACE . . . . Page 30

Regent; Mr. Lewis.

Mr. Smith's horse could not have won, because the horse that won was black.

Mr. Bailey's horse did not win.

Therefore, Mr. Lewis's horse must have won.

Tally-ho could not have won, because he broke his ankle at the start, and so could not have been Mr. Lewis's horse.

Sonny Boy could not have been Mr. Lewis's horse because he had previously run.

Therefore, Regent must have been Mr. Lewis's horse, and the winner of the race.

THE SOCCER LEAGUE . . . . Page 31

Since the four teams each play the other three teams once, there are six matches in all, and hence a total of 12 points to be awarded. Now we know that United scored five points, Hotspur scored three points, and Villa scored one point, whence it follows that Arsenal scored three points.

But Arsenal scored no goals at all; therefore, they tied all their matches.

We can now construct most of our "League Standings."

	GOALS				STANDINGS			
	A.	H.	U.	V.	W.	L.	T.	Pts.
Arsenal	—	0	0	0	0	0	3	3
Hotspur	0	—	3	4	1	1	1	3
United	0	4	—	1	2	0	1	5
Villa	0	1	0	—	0	2	1	1

Hotspur must have scored three goals against United (they have seven goals altogether), and yet were beaten; United also beat Villa. United has only five goals in all, since 13 were scored altogether and eight are accounted for above. Hence United beat Hotspur 4-3, and beat Villa

LATE FOR TEE . . . . Page 32

Mac figured to arrive at eight o'clock. He arrived two hours or 120 minutes later than he would have had he maintained his average speed of 60 miles per hour.

If he had gone along without mishap it would have taken him one minute to traverse each mile. At 15 miles per hour it took him four minutes to traverse each mile. Therefore, he lost three minutes each mile traveled after the trouble started.

Since he lost two hours or 120 minutes, his car must have been in distress the last 40 miles of the trip. This means, then, that he had traveled 80 miles before his engine started to kick up a fuss.

At 60 miles per hour, it must have taken him 80 minutes to do 80 miles. Since he left at six in the morning, his car must have developed engine trouble at 7:20.

THE MARINERS . . . . Page 33

The *Hispaniola;* Cherbourg.

Brine is Captain of the *Albatross* because he was host to Tarr on that ship.

It is obvious from the statement about Mrs. Salt that her husband's ship has not been in dry dock just previous to this trip, because she was taken off his ship eight days ago when it landed.

Therefore, Salt's ship cannot be the *Hispaniola,* which has been in dry dock for seven weeks, and must be the *Americus.*

Tarr's ship then is the *Hispaniola.*

The last statement shows that the *Americus* is headed for Liverpool.

The *Albatross* must be headed for New York because the fact that it shipped a stowaway back by the *Americus* proves that it was going in the opposite direction to the *Americus.*

Therefore, the *Hispaniola* must be bound for Cherbourg.

THE FORTY-TWO BEERS . . . . Page 34

Who paid for the beers? Why the American, of course! There is no disputing the fact that he paid currency each time he bought a drink. The point is that he increased the value of the currency which he got in return; that is, he increased the 90¢ change he got on each transaction by walking across the border. He added value to the currency by transferring it from one place to another.

There is nothing more startling about this increase in value than there is about buying an object in China that is worth 10¢ there, and transporting it to America where it is worth 50¢. The American who performed the work of carrying a Guatelavian dollar from Tinto to Guatelavia performed 10¢ worth of work from the viewpoint of economics.

Twenty-six feet. Let x equal the length of the ladder; let y equal the height of the wall. Then, for the shaded portion of the triangle below, we have the equation:

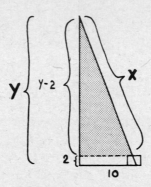

$$x^2 = (y-2)^2 + 10^2$$

We know that the length of the ladder is equal to the height of the wall. Thus, $x = y$ and the above equation becomes:

$$y^2 = (y-2)^2 + 10^2$$
$$y = 26 \text{ feet}$$

The artist's problem can be solved by cutting the canvas

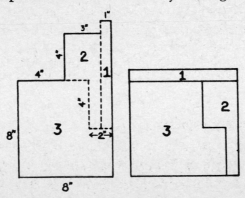

into three pieces as shown. This results in a square nine inches on a side, containing a total of 81 square inches.

THE COMMUTER . . . . Page 38

The chauffeur, meeting Brown at some point between the residence and the station, saves 20 minutes from his usual trip by not being obliged to proceed from the point where Brown is met to the station and then *make a return trip* to that point. In other words, the chauffeur saves the run of double the distance from the point where Brown is met, to the station. The saving, amounting to 20 minutes in all, means a saving of two 10 minute runs. Therefore, the chauffeur met Brown 10 minutes before he would usually arrive at the station. Since he usually arrived at 5 p.m., he met Brown at 4:50 p.m. Since Brown arrived at the station at 4 p.m. and was met at 4:50 p.m., he walked 50 minutes.

THE HORSE TRADER . . . . Page 39

Twenty-nine horses. This problem is very easy if you work it backwards. The trader had one horse on which to ride home. He disposed of the next to the last horse as a trading fee when he exited from the third fair. This makes a total of two. Since he sold half of his remaining string at the fair, he must have had four in order to have had two left. He paid one to get in. So he must have arrived at the last fair with *five* horses.

It's a simple matter to follow through in reverse and figure out that he started business with 29 horses.

MURDER IN THE LIBRARY . . . . Page 40

If the night watchman, in passing Mr. Parker's house, had seen Mr. Parker commit suicide in his library at 7:30 P.M. on January 2, the light in that room must have been burning; yet, the watchman stated that he had turned it on when he entered the room.

COUNT THE TRAINS . . . . **Page 42**

Thirteen trains. Since it takes six hours to make the trip from Washington to New York, the train which is pulling into New York as Tom's train leaves left Washington at 5 a.m. Tom will arrive in Washington six hours later, or at 5 p.m. He will therefore pass trains which left or will leave Washington at the following hours: 5 a.m.–6 a.m.–7 a.m.–8 a.m.–9 a.m.–10 a.m.–11 a.m.–12 n.–1 p.m.–2 p.m.–3 p.m.–4 p.m. Of course, at the exact moment his train pulls into the Washington station, a train will be leaving for New York. If he is alert, he will also see this one. The answer then is 13 trains.

SUBURBS . . . . **Page 43**

Set out the data as follows, using x, y, and z to represent the unknowns.

Name	Resides at	Works at
x	S	R
R	—	B
y	B	x
E	—	y
z	—	—

In any line down or across, each capital letter may appear only once. Then clearly x = T. Therefore, y = S, and z = B. Mr. Blackheath must work at Ealing.

THE FIVE PEDAGOGUES . . . . **Page 44**

This is a very simple problem if one works it out diagrammatically. The subjects taught by the five pedagogues are shown in the chart below:

INSTRUCTORS	SUBJECTS				
Mr. Botany		G		H	
Mr. Geometry	B				S
Mr. French	B	G			
Mr. History			F		S
Mr. Syntax			F	H	

THE STEEL BEAM . . . . Page 45

The ¾-pound weight is equal to ¼ of a beam. Therefore, the beam must weigh four times ¾ of a pound, or three pounds.

JUGGLING JUGS . . . . Page 46

First step: From the biggest jug, which now contains 8 quarts of oil, pour 5 quarts into the 5-quart jug. This leaves 3 quarts in the biggest jug.

Second step: Take the jug that has 5 quarts in it, and pour 3 quarts into the smallest jug.

Third Step: Take the 3 quarts from the smallest jug and pour it into the largest jug. You now have 6 quarts in the largest jug, 2 quarts in the middle-size jug, and nothing in the smallest jug.

Fourth step: Pour the 2 quarts from the middle-size jug into the smallest jug. The middle-size jug is now empty. There are 6 quarts in the largest jug and 2 quarts in the smallest jug.

Fifth step:	From the largest jug, fill the middle-size jug. The three jugs now contain the following: the largest jug has 1 quart; the middle-size jug has 5 quarts; and the smallest jug has 2 quarts.
Sixth step:	Pour 1 quart from the middle-size jug into the smallest jug. That leaves 1 quart in the largest jug; 4 quarts in the middle-size jug; and 3 quarts in the smallest jug.
Seventh step:	Pour the 3 quarts from the smallest jug into the largest jug. You now have 4 quarts in each of the two larger jugs.

THE SMALL GAME HUNTERS . . . . . . Page 47

Since rabbits have four feet and quail have two feet, the two gentlemen must have shot four rabbits and 13 quail. This would account for 17 heads, 16 rabbit feet, and 26 quail feet. Since four rabbits were shot, and both hunters bagged an equal number, each must have shot two rabbits. Robert claims he shot three times as many quail as rabbits. This means that he shot six quail. Therefore, Gerald shot seven quail.

THE FRATERNITY CONVENTION . . . . . . Page 48

MR. GROCER IS THE BAKER.

MR. BUTCHER IS THE LAWYER.

MR. DOCTOR IS THE ARTIST.

MR. ARTIST IS THE BUTCHER.

MR. BAKER IS THE DOCTOR.

MR. LAWYER IS THE GROCER.

Mr. Butcher, addressing Mr. Grocer, says that he heard that Mr. Grocer mashed his finger at his store under a tub of butter. Now, Mr. Grocer, having a store, is either a baker, a butcher, or a grocer. He cannot be a grocer because no man bears the name of his trade. A tub of butter would be found in a bakery but not in a butcher shop. *Therefore, Mr. Grocer is a baker.*

Mr. Artist cannot be either the doctor or the grocer because he would not refer to them in the third person, and Mr. Artist cannot be the baker because we have already established that Mr. Grocer is the baker. Mr. Artist cannot be the artist, because no man bears the name of his profession. Therefore, Mr. Artist must be either the lawyer or the butcher. We can be sure that he is not the lawyer because Mr. Doctor, while talking to him mentions the lawyer, as if he were some other person. *Therefore, Mr. Artist must be the butcher.*

Mr. Doctor states that he goes deep-sea fishing with the lawyer every week. Mr. Doctor cannot be the butcher or the baker because Mr. Grocer has already been established as the baker and Mr. Artist has been established as the butcher. Again, the man who goes deep-sea fishing with the lawyer cannot be the doctor because it is Mr. Doctor who is talking and Mr. Doctor is not a doctor. Therefore, the lawyer goes deep-sea fishing with either the grocer or the artist.

But the lawyer does not go deep-sea fishing each week-end with the grocer who lives in Milwaukee. This fact becomes evident when it is realized that Milwaukee is situated inland more than 1,000 miles from either the East Coast or the West Coast of the United States and from the Gulf of Mexico. It would be impossible for a resident of Milwaukee to take a weekend trip each week to do deep-sea fishing. Therefore, by elimination, the lawyer goes deep-sea fishing with the artist. *This establishes Mr. Doctor as the artist.*

We still must determine who is the doctor, who is the lawyer, and who is the grocer. We can infer, however, that two of these men live in the same town.

The doctor lives in Milwaukee; the grocer lives in Milwaukee. The lawyer lives on the seacoast. Mr. Baker, talking to Mr. Lawyer, mentions that he got in a new interesting case at the office. He says that he will tell him about it during next week. This argues very strongly that Mr. Baker lives in the same city as Mr. Lawyer. It must be remembered that the Convention has been in session for a full week at St. Louis. Therefore, the lawyer presumably would leave for either the East Coast or the West Coast or the Gulf at the close of the Convention. In any event, his route home could not possibly take him through Milwaukee. Moreover, he has just seen his friends and has already taken a week's vacation and there is no reason to believe that he is going off another few hundred miles simply to visit. This reasoning points to the fact that the man who says so casually that he will drop in to tell Mr. Baker about his new interesting case during the week must be the doctor who lives with the grocer in Milwaukee. *This establishes the doctor as Mr. Baker, and the grocer as Mr. Lawyer.*

Of course, then, Mr. Butcher is the lawyer. His interest in the baker's mashed finger could have been actuated by other than professional motives. He could simply have been interested in determining how serious an accident his fraternity brother, the baker, had sustained. Moreover, since he has asked the baker to play golf with him during the week, it is very likely that they, too, live near each other. There is nothing to indicate that the baker does not actually live in the same town with the lawyer.

THE CHECKERBOARD · · · · · · · · **Page 50**

The diagram below shows the solution to the problem.

DIRTY FACES . . . . **Page 51**

The two boys had seen each other's face. Each naturally assumed that his own resembled the other's.

THE PENSIONER . . . . **Page 52**

Ninety years old. Let x equal the man's present age. We can set up the following equation:

$$x = 4\frac{1}{2} + 1/6\,x + 1/5\,x + 1/4\,x + 1/3\,x$$
$$x = 90$$

THE CAT IN THE WELL . . . . **Page 53**

Thirty-one minutes. In the first two minutes, the cat climbed one foot. In 30 minutes, the cat climbed 15 feet. During the next minute, the cat would have gained the necessary three feet to reach the top. Once at the top of the well, there would be no more sliding back.

A SQUARE IN LINDLAND . . . . **Page 54**

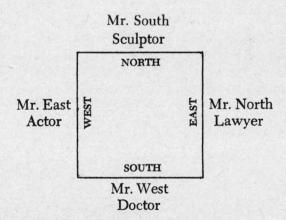

Mr. South
Sculptor

Mr. East
Actor

Mr. North
Lawyer

Mr. West
Doctor

It is at once deducible that the sculptor is Mr. South. The rest follows.

THE DRY GOODS DEALER . . . . **Page 55**

The dry goods dealer takes the piece of material and stretches it along the edge of a piece of paper, marking off five yards on the paper. He then adds the 36-inch width to the five-yard measurement, making a total of six yards marked off on the paper. He folds the paper in half, which gives him a three-yard measure, and then folds this three-yard measure in half, which gives him a yard-and-a-half measure. He then cuts the five-yard piece of material to the point indicated by the yard-and-a-half measure.

THE ROPE LADDER . . . . **Page 56**

Five rungs—for as the tide rises, the yacht will, of course, rise with it. The ladder, being attached to the yacht, will rise with the boat.

THE TEACHER'S DILEMMA . . . . **Page 57**

Twelve students can be seated in the classroom as shown.

THE SIX AUTHORS . . . . **Page 58**

White, essayist
Brown, poet
Green, humorist

Pink, historian
Gray, playwright
Black, novelist

THE DIFFICULT CROSSING . . . . **Page 59**

Four trips. First he takes the duck over, leaving the dog alone with the corn. Then he takes the dog over and brings back the duck. Then he brings the corn over and leaves the corn with the dog. Then he comes back for the duck.

THE FOUR GOATS . . . . **Page 60**

One hundred feet. Before the farmer sells three goats, the area grazed by one goat is equal to one-quarter of a circle with a radius of 50 feet. The area of such a circle is $50^2 \pi$ square feet. One goat, then, grazes over $2,500 \pi \div 4$ square feet, and all four goats graze over a combined area of $2,500 \pi$ square feet.

The remaining goat grazes over an area equal to one-quarter of a circle whose area is $r^2 \pi$, where r equals the length of the tether as well as the radius of this circle.

$$\text{Thus, } \tfrac{1}{4} r^2 \pi = 2,500 \pi$$
$$r = 100 \text{ feet}$$

THE DARING YOUNG MAN . . . . **Page 61**

He juggles the balls. This way, one ball is always in mid-air, and the bridge only has to support 199 pounds at any given moment.

THE COUNTERFEIT COIN . . . . **Page 62**

Two. The wise man divided the nine coins into three groups of three. First he weighed Group A against Group B. If they balanced, then he knew that each of the coins in these groups were of the same weight, and therefore each of these six coins were made of pure gold.

The counterfeit would then be found in the last group of three. He then took any two of the last three remaining coins, and put one of these two coins on each side of the scale. If these two coins balanced, then the counterfeit coin would have to be the last unweighed coin. If the two coins did not balance, then of course, the lighter coin—the one on the scale that went up—would be the counterfeit coin.

Now suppose that in the first instance, when weighing the two groups of three, one side of the scale went up. It would then be clear that the lighter coin was among this group of three. The sage would then proceed, as stated above, with the three coins among which the lightest one was to be found.

THE PROBLEM OF THE CHAINS . . . . . .

The cheapest way to make a continuous 30-link chain out of the six five-link pieces is to open up all five links of one piece, then use these five links to join the remaining five pieces. The cost of this chain would be $3.50, 50 cents less than the cost of a brand new continuous chain.

THE OHIO LIMITED . . . .

Brown is the engineer.

The guard lives halfway between Cleveland and New York. He cannot earn one-third of Mr. Jones's salary, because that sum cannot be divided into three equal parts. Mr. Robinson lives in Cleveland. Therefore, Mr. Brown must be the guard's neighbor.

Since Mr. Jones must therefore live in New York, the guard is Jones. Brown cannot be the fireman, so he must be the engineer.

THE STYMIED SAVAGE . . . .

The missionary said, "I will die by fire." If the medicine man judged the statement to be true, he would be forced to have him shot. This would make the statement false. For a false statement, the missionary would indeed be burned to death. But this would make the statement true, and then he would have to be shot instead. The only way out of this vicious circle was to let the clever missionary go free.

NARROW ESCAPE . . . . Page 66

The fallacy is that Mr. Drake, who must have been looking out the window on the right side of his car to see any possible damage, could not have seen the sun on that side while he was traveling north.

THE SAHARA EXPEDITION . . . . Page 67

The car, of course, has four wheels, so that for a 27,000-mile journey it uses up 108,000 tire miles. Each tire is good for 12,000 miles, and mathematically *nine* tires will suffice.

The real problem is: How can the explorer get through the trip with this minimum number? The first four tires will be used up and discarded after 12,000 miles, one of the five remaining will have to be changed each 3,000 miles as follows: First 3,000 miles—Tires 1, 2, 3, 4; second 3,000 miles—Tires 2, 3, 4, 5; Third 3,000 miles—Tires 3, 4, 5, 1; fourth 3,000 miles—Tires 4, 5, 1, 2; fifth 3,000 miles—Tires 5, 1, 2, 3.

Thus each of the nine tires will be used no more than 12,000 miles.

TRACKS IN THE SNOW . . . . Page 68

The tracks were made by a peg-legged man wheeling a wheelbarrow. Between the footprint and the impression made by the butt end of a wooden stump, lies the track of the wheel of the wheelbarrow. At one point, toward the middle of the trail, there is evidence that the man paused to rest. The prints left by the two wheelbarrow butts are there to show this. They are wider apart and larger than the tracks left by the man. While the man rested, he brought his foot and wooden leg parallel. Then he lifted the wheelbarrow and started off again.

E pushes B into C. E returns to the main line, then pushes A and couples it to B. E then draws A and B out into the right siding. E uncouples, goes into segment C, and pushes A out on to the main line, leaving B in the right siding. E comes around and picks up A and pushes it up into left siding, then returns to the main line.

The blind man reasoned thus: If there were a black hat on my head and a black hat on the head of the second speaker, then the first man addressed would have seen two black hats. He would have then drawn the inescapable conclusion that his own hat was white .

Similarly, if there were a black hat on my head and a black hat on the head of the first man addressed, then the second speaker would have known that his own hat was white. Since neither of these men were able to draw any conclusion, it is clear that I do not wear a black hat *in combination with someone else wearing a black hat*.

The only question left then for me is: Do I *alone* wear a black hat? If I were, the second speaker would see it and would have been able to definitely conclude the color of his own hat. The second speaker would have said to himself, "My hat is not black, for if it were, the first speaker would have seen two black hats and would have known that *his* hat was white. Therefore, my hat cannot be black."

But the second speaker was not able to draw this conclusion. He could only have failed to do this because he did not see a black hat on my head. Therefore, since I and another do not wear black hats and since I do not wear a black hat all by myself, there must be a white hat on my head.

Winner—C. J. Smith
Runner-up—Reynolds
Third—Fellows
Fourth—P. F. Smith

We immediately observe that the runner-up had been a cripple since youth. Then neither of the athletic Smith twins could possibly have been runner-up. It is apparent, then, that either Reynolds or Fellows finished second.

Reynolds defeated Fellows. It is impossible, then, that Fellows could have finished better than second. But the runner-up was not married, and Fellows was married; consequently, Fellows could not have been the runner-up and must have finished third or fourth. Bearing in mind that the runner-up position had to go to either Reynolds or Fellows, and discovering that it could not have gone to Fellows, we are able to locate Reynolds as the runner-up.

Fellows, we have discovered, finished either third or fourth. If we assume that he was fourth, then the Smith twins must have been first and third; but this is obviously impossible because the man who finished third had never previously met the winner. Our assumption, then, cannot be correct, and Fellows had to finish in third position.

Now we know that Reynolds was second and that Fellows was third. The winner must have been one of the Smiths, and he must have been the one who had never previously met Fellows. P. F. Smith had been an usher at Fellows' wedding. Therefore, the winner must have been C. J. Smith. P. F. Smith could have finished only in fourth position.

THE CLIMBING MONKEY . . . . **Page 72**

The monkey and the weight always remain opposite. The

monkey cannot rise above or sink below the height of the weight, for the two are perfectly balanced.

THE SWISS MILKMAIDS . . . . Page 73

All the milk cans are manufactured by the same can company, and are of the same size, since all are labeled *No. 10*. But Geraldine's milk can, having a dent in it, obviously holds less milk than the others. Since its cubic content is less, it must weigh less than either of the other two cans.

Molly's milk can weighs most. At the top of the mountain, from where she came, her milk can weighed 11 pounds. On that high location, it weighed exactly the same as Jenny's milk can did in the valley. It is a well-established fact that an object weighs less on a mountain than it does at sea level. Therefore, if Molly's milk can weighed 11 pounds on the mountain, it would weigh more than 11 pounds when she brought it down to the valley. So Molly's milk can weighs the most and Geraldine's weighs the least.

FATHEAD'S FARM . . . . Page 74

Mr. Shepherd is the driver and his son assists Mr. Driver. Mr. Driver is the carter and his son assists Mr. Carter. Mr. Ploughman is the shepherd and his son assists Mr. Shepherd.
Mr. Carter is the ploughman and his son assists Mr. Ploughman.

THE LILY POND . . . . Page 75

Twenty days. If the lily doubles its area every day, then on the day before it has covered the entire pond it must have covered an area equal to one-half the area of the pond. It covers the entire pond in 21 days; thus it covers half the pond in 20 days.

THE BLIND BUTLER Page 76

Three socks.

THE VICTORY COLUMN . . . . Page 77

Two hundred and fifty feet. If you take a sheet of paper
and mark it with a diagonal line, as in figure A, you will
find that when you roll it into a cylindrical form, with
the line outside, it will appear as in figure B. It will be
seen that the spiral (in one complete turn) is merely the
hypotenuse of a right triangle, of which the length and
width of the paper are the other two sides.

In the puzzle presented, the lengths of the two sides
of the triangle are 40 feet (one-fifth of 200 feet) and
30 feet. Therefore the hypotenuse is 50 feet. The length
of the garland is therefore five times as long, or 250 feet.

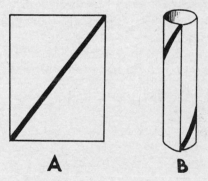

A   B

THE RIDDLE OF THE RED WINE . . . . . . Page 78

The same quantity of wine was transferred from the
bottle as water was taken from the jug. Let us assume
that the glass would hold a quarter of a pint. After the
first manipulation the bottle contains three-quarters of a
pint of wine, and the jug one pint of water mixed with a
quarter of a pint of wine. Now, the second transaction

consists in taking away a fifth of the contents of the jug, that is, one-fifth of a pint of water mixed with one-fifth of a quarter of a pint of wine. We thus leave behind in the jug four-fifths of a quarter of a pint of wine (one-fifth of a pint) while we transfer from the jug to the bottle an equal quantity (one-fifth of a pint) of water.

THE VANISHED COIN . . . . Page 79

The coin which had been inadvertently mislaid was a great rarity. The stranger, being a collector of antiques and coins, happened to have in his vest pocket the only other specimen extant of the coin which Lewis had brought from the Continent. If the stranger submitted to a search of his person, the prize coin would have been found upon him and he would have been accused of stealing it. If he resisted the accusation of theft, his own coin would have been taken from him, since all would have avowed that the coin belonged to Lewis. The stranger did not wish to lose his own valuable coin. The reason that the stranger did not exhibit his own coin to the assembled guests in the first instance was that since he was an invited guest it would have been a breach of propriety to steal the show from Lewis, who was a member and inordinately proud of his prize find.

THE EGG MAN . . . . Page 81

271 eggs.

THE STOLEN NECKLACE . . . . Page 82

Bill is telling the whole truth. Hank says that he upset the inkwell. But there is no stain of any kind on the blotter, so his statement is obviously false. Clark says that he walked to the phone and *quickly* dialed Police Headquarters, in the dark. If one is very familiar with a dial telephone, it is entirely possible to dial a number in the dark—but it is not possible to do so *quickly*. Sid's misstatement consists of saying that it was pitch black and he could see the cat's eyes gleaming in the dark. Cat's eyes do not gleam in total darkness. It is true that they are able to reflect even the smallest ray of light, which is usually present even at night, but if it were pitch black, the cat's eyes could not gleam. By the process of elimination, only Bill remains; and indeed there is nothing he says that is contradicted by fact, so we may assume he is telling the whole truth.

THE FOOTBALL TOURNAMENT . . . . . . Page 83

From statement (1), we know that Albie's team made its only score in the final game by a touchdown; from statement (4), the purple team scored only a field goal in this game. Therefore, Albie's team beat the purple team 6-3 in the play-off.

Statement (3) shows that Ben's team survived the first round by defeating Tulane, and must therefore have been the purple team that was defeated by Albie's team in the play-off.

Knowing the above facts, and statements (3) and (6), we can now bracket the teams thus:

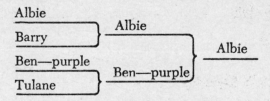

It is now obvious that Bill must have been captain of Tulane.

We see that Tulane was the only team that Albie's team did not meet. Statement (7) proves that Tulane was the brown team.

147

From statement (2), it is apparent that the red team must have been Barry's and that Albie's team was Tufts.

Since we have found that the red, purple, and brown teams were Barry's, Ben's, and Bill's respectively, Albie's team must have been blue.

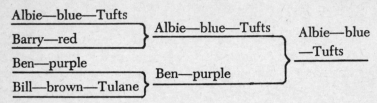

As Trinity did not play Ben's team, the brackets show us that Trinity was Barry's team.

Therefore, Ben's team must have been Temple, and the complete brackets look like this:

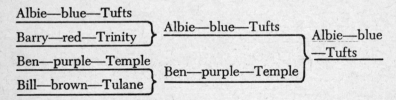

THE MUNICIPAL RAILWAYS . . . . Page 84

The illustration shows the required directions for the five lines, so that no line shall ever cross another.

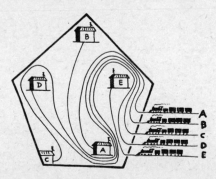

THE SIMPLE-MINDED MAID . . . . Page 85

It was not necessary for the maid, having discovered that the fourth letter was *I*, to ascertain what *I* stood for.

THE BLIND ABBOT . . . . Page 86

18 monks

1	0	8
0		0
8	0	1

20 monks

4	1	4
1		1
4	1	4

24 monks

3	3	3
3		3
3	3	3

32 monks

1	7	1
7		7
1	7	1

36 monks

0	9	0
9		9
0	9	0

Ace of Spades; Queen of Hearts; Six of Clubs.

Geoffrey Warren was considered the foremost appraiser in London. His sales were based on the reputation of his firm for both integrity and knowledge. While polishing the cameo to which he had given such unstinted praise, he discovered that it was a forgery. He had to prevent the terrible discovery from being made by anyone else. A firm like Warren and Company couldn't afford to be mistaken. They were highly reputable and were expected to know what was genuine and what was bogus. Geoffrey Warren stole the cameo to destroy it. His reputation was worth more than £5,000.

Rudolph murdered Robert.

The first statement makes it plain that Robert's brother is the murderer, and Robert then is innocent.

Ralph cannot be Robert's brother because he has met Robert's father only once. Therefore, Ralph is not guilty.

Since Ronald, the host, is about to give evidence against the murderer, he cannot be the murderer.

Therefore, Rudolph must be the murderer.

Since the host, Ronald, is about to give evidence, he must still be alive; and Rudolph, the murderer, obviously cannot be the victim.

This leaves as the murdered man either Robert or Ralph.

Since Ralph is a cripple and Rudolph has known Ronald for only five days, Ralph and Rudolph are the men with whom Ronald did not customarily bowl; so one of them must have eaten with the murdered man on the night previous to the murder. Rudolph was in jail and so it was not he. Then Ralph must have eaten with the victim.

Ralph then is not the victim, and since Rudolph and Ronald have both been previously eliminated, Robert is obviously the murdered man.

THE HANGING SCALES . . . . Page 93

Eight spoons. On Scale No. 4, we find that the pitcher is balanced by two glasses. But since, according to Scale No. 2, two plates will balance a glass, we can deduce that the weight of a pitcher is equal to the weight of four plates.

If this is so, then by removing equal weights from both sides of Scale No. 1, that is, a pitcher from the left hand side and four plates from the right hand side, we shall not disturb the balance. We are thus able to show that one glass will be balanced by two cups.

If then we substitute on Scale No. 3 two glasses for the pitcher, we will have two glasses on the left side equalling a glass and two cups on the right side, which will leave three plates to balance six spoons. Therefore, the weight of one plate is equal to the weight of two spoons.

Since, according to Scale No. 2, a glass is equal to two plates, and since a glass is equal to two cups, the weight of a plate is equal to the weight of a cup. We can thus remove the plate and the cup from Scale No. 5 without disturbing the weight ratio. Since a plate will be balanced by two spoons, a glass, according to Scale No. 2, should be balanced by four spoons. Consequently, two glasses will be balanced by eight spoons.

THE FRUIT PEDDLERS . . . . Page 94

The peddlers all had this sign on their pushcarts

Apples
3 for 10¢

The first peddler, who had fifteen apples, sold his apples to five customers at three for a dime, thus receiving fifty cents. The second peddler sold nine of his apples to three customers at three for a dime, thus receiving thirty cents, and then sold five customers a single apple each at four cents apiece, thus receiving twenty cents, or a total of fifty cents.

The statement that a sale at four cents each is at a "three-for-ten-cents" rate cannot reasonably be challenged. If you are unconvinced, go to a market and attempt to buy a single item which is marked "three-for-ten" at less than four cents.

The third peddler sold three of his apples to one customer for a dime, and then made ten individual sales at four cents each. He, too, realized the sum of fifty cents.

The same result ensues if we postulate a market sign of "six-for-a-quarter." Here, of course, the individual sale of a single apple would be made at a rate of five cents apiece. The total yield under these conditions for each peddler would be sixty-five cents.

MRS. ADDEM'S CHILDREN . . . . Page 95

Let Mrs. Addem's age equal a, and let the sum of her children's ages be s. We can formulate two equations from the data:

$$a = 3s$$
$$a + 11 = s + 33, \text{ which is the same as:}$$
$$a = s + 22$$
$$\text{Then, } 3s = s + 22$$
$$s = 11$$

The children's ages total 11. Since no two of them were born in the same year, they can only be 6, 3, and 2.

FIGHT TO THE FINISH . . . . Page 96

Dan is Tim's cousin. Bill is wearing colored trunks. Mike says his son is the fighter.

David won the scholarship with 83 marks. The marks were distributed as set out below.

	SUBJECTS					TOTAL MARKS
	L	E	S	M	H	
Alfred	3/12	1/27	4/10	5/1	2/13	63
Bertram	1/14	5/1	2/12	4/2	3/12	41
Cyril	2/13	4/2	3/11	1/20	5/10	56
David	5/10	2/26	1/18	3/18	4/11	83
Egbert	4/11	3/4	5/9	2/19	1/14	57

Spud was the murderer. The judge reasoned as follows:

A) Dan is innocent because he couldn't be the murderer if either of his statements is true.

B) Mat is innocent for the same reason.

C) Red is innocent because if we assume that he is guilty the following statements become true:

> *Red:* Me and Mike were together from 10 to 12 away from the rest of the gang.
>
> *Mike:* I never saw a gun in my life.
>
> *Jim:* All of us except Dan were in Chi when it happened.

In view of this true statement by Jim, Spud's second sentence becomes false, rendering his first one true

> Spud: Only one of us witnessed the murder. Now since the murder was witnessed, and since Red and Mike were together at the time, Mike must have been the witness. But this leads to a contradiction in view of Mike's true statement.

D) Jim is innocent because if we assume that he is guilty the following statements become true:

> Jim: All of us except Dan were in Chi when it happened.
>
> Spud: Only one of us witnessed the murder.
>
> Dan: I was in Philly when it happened.
>
> Mat: I was at the neighborhood movies, at the time, with some other one of the boys.
>
> Red: Me and Mike were together from 10 to 12 away from the rest of the gang.

These statements are contradictory because Mat's statement above can't possibly be true in view of the above facts. With whom did Mat go to the movies? Not with Red, Mike, or Dan, according to the foregoing. Obviously, it couldn't have been with the murderer, Jim. And Mat specifically excluded Spud as his companion. He said "Spud's the murderer. I was at the neighborhood movies, at the time, when *some other one* of the boys." If this last statement is held true, then the assumption of Jim's guilt must be dropped.

E) Mike is innocent because if we assume that he is guilty then the following statements become true:

> Dan: I was in Philly when it happened.
>
> Mat: I was at the neighborhood movies, at the time, with some other one of the boys.
>
> Red: Me and Mike were together from 10 to 12 away from the rest of the gang.

If Mike was the murderer and Mike and Red were alone when the woman was shot, then Red must have been the sole witness. This makes Spud's statement: "Only one of us witnessed the murder," a true statement. Spud, then, must have made a false statement when he said: "I was not even in town on the night of the killing." Of course, then, Spud *was in Chicago* on the night of the murder. So was Mat. He went to the neighborhood movies with "some other one of the boys." With whom? His statement specifically excluded Spud as his companion; Dan was in Philly; Red and Mike were at the scene of the crime; therefore, the only one of the boys that could have been at the movies with Mat would have been Jim. This analysis places all the men in Chicago on the night of the murder, with the exception of Dan. If this is so, then Jim's statement: "All of us except Dan were in Chi when it happened" must be true, rendering Jim's first statement "Mike pulled the trigger" false.

F) Spud is the guilty man. He is so proved through a process of elimination. Although he cannot be directly proved to be guilty, no statement or fact conflicts with the theory of his guilt. Since one of the men is guilty by hypothesis, it must be he. Assuming Spud guilty, the following statements become true:

Dan: I was in Philly when it happened.
Jim: All of us except Dan were in Chi when it happened.
Spud: Only one of us witnessed the murder.
Red: Me and Mike were away from the rest of the gang when it happened.

Who was the witness? Well, either Mat or Jim. For if Spud is guilty, Mat's statement: "I was at the movies, at the time, with some other one of the boys," becomes false.

SMOKE GETS IN YOUR EYES . . . . **Page 100**

Six cigarettes. Five cigarettes can be made from the 25 butts. After these are smoked, there will be five more butts. From these five butts, a sixth cigarette can be made.

Brown, Jr., could not have been the politician (statement 2).

Since Smith, Sr., because of being a paralytic, could not have played golf (statement 4), and since the politician's father played golf (statement 3), Smith, Jr., could not have been the politician.

If neither Brown, Jr., nor Smith, Jr., was the politician, Jones, Jr., must have been he.

Statement 1 tells us that the lawyer frequently played tennis with his father. Because Smith, Sr., could not have played tennis (statement 4), Smith, Jr., could not have been the lawyer. We have previously discovered that he was not the politician. He must, then, have been the banker.

Since Jones, Jr., was the politician and Smith, Jr, was the banker, Brown, Jr., must have been the lawyer.

THE FIVE OFFICE BOYS . . . . **Page 102**

	R	W	A	G	H	TOTAL PTS.
Percy	2	3	4	3	0	12
Walter	1	2	3	4	1	11
Fred	4	1	1	2	2	10
Cyril	0	4	2	0	3	9
Foch	3	0	0	1	4	8

A CASE OF ORANGES . . . . **Page 103**

Let m equal the number of oranges Mary has. Let j equal the number Jane has, k the number Kate has, and e the number Eliza has. We can then formulate four equations:

(1) $m = j + 20$, and therefore $j = m - 20$

(2) $m = k + 53$, and therefore $k = m - 53$
(3) $m = e + 71$, and therefore $e = m - 71$
(4) $m + j + k + e = 233$

Substituting for j, k, and e in equation (4), we find that $m = 94\frac{1}{4}$ oranges.

So, the remaining oranges are divided thus: Jane has $74\frac{1}{4}$, Kate has $41\frac{1}{4}$, and Eliza has $23\frac{1}{4}$.

IT REALLY HAPPENED ONE NIGHT . . . . . Page 104

On close consideration of the facts, it is apparent that Winston's objective was to waken Malcolm solely for the purpose of *awakening him*. He never intended to communicate with him. Nor did he.

The only reason that Winston could have for wishing to accomplish his apparent mischief was that Malcolm, by sleeping, was doing *him* a mischief. You see, Winston and Malcolm were both tenants in the same apartment house, and Winston's bedroom adjoined Malcolm's. Malcolm was snoring so loudly that Winston couldn't fall asleep. The victim's only chance, which he cleverly saw, was to disturb the disturber and beat him to the snooze.

BOOTS . . . . Page 105

Four dollars and a pair of boots.

THE LOST COIN . . . . Page 106

Paul is the rightful owner of the coin. While a person does not lose his right of ownership merely because he drops something on another person's land, Bill's statement that he dropped this same coin on this same spot four months ago is not convincing. Both he and Dan agree that the coin glitters. But a coin buried beneath the sand for so long would lose its sparkle. Therefore, we may conclude that Bill is lying. As for Sam and Brad, they are mistaken about the law. Seeing or finding something does not in itself confer ownership. Paul is right. He owns the land; therefore, he owns everything on it.

THE CARETAKER . . . . Page 107

The man could not have hanged himself without something by which to climb to the high chandelier, but it is specified that the room was vacant. Therefore, he must have been hanged by someone else, who had later removed the evidence that would readily suggest a murder.

THE STOLEN ANTIQUE . . . . Page 108

Mrs. Black.

Mr. Brown won money at cards; therefore, from the first statement, we know that Mrs. Brown was not the thief.

Since Mrs. Brown played cards, the other female guest referred to in the third statement must have been Mrs. White.

Since Mrs. Black and Mrs. White did not play cards, neither of their husbands could have been the thief.

If Mr. Brown had paralysis of the hands and arms, he could not have played golf with Mr. Black; therefore, Mr. Brown could not have been the thief.

This eliminates all but Mrs. Black and Mrs. White.

Since Mr. Black had not previously met Mrs. White, Mrs. White could not have been the one with whom Mr. Black had played golf that day; therefore, Mrs. White could not have been the thief. By elimination, Mrs. Black must have been the thief.

THE MAILBOX . . . . Page 109

No. Contango was just as much to blame as his secretary. His key was delivered in the locked mailbox.

THE ADVENTUROUS SNAIL . . . . Page 110

Twenty days.

At the end of 17 days the snail will have climbed 17 feet, and at the end of the 18th day it will be at the top of the wall. It instantly begins slipping while sleeping, and will be two feet down the other side at the end of the 18th night. How long will it take to travel the remaining 18 feet? If it slips two feet at night it clearly overcomes the tendency to slip two feet during the daytime, in climbing up. (In rowing up a river we have the stream against us, but in coming down it is with us and helps us.) If the snail can climb three feet and overcome the tendency to slip two feet in 12 hours' ascent, it could with the same exertion crawl five feet a day on the level. Therefore, in going down, the same exertion carries the snail seven feet in 12 hours; that is, five feet by personal exertion and two feet by slip. This, with the night slip, gives it a descending progress of nine feet in 24 hours. It can therefore do the remaining 18 feet in exactly two days, and the whole journey up and down will take the snail exactly 20 days.

THE FOUR COEDS . . . . Page 111

Joan is the oldest, then Jane, Jean, and June.

THE DEAD TOURIST . . . . Page 112

Seeing Mrs. Elkins' picture in the Boston society column, and reading the details of the tragic death of her husband, Mr. Harper remembered that Mrs. Elkins had been to his travel bureau to purchase tickets for a European trip. Examining the files, he discovered that she had bought one round-trip ticket and one one-way ticket. This led him to believe that she never expected Mr. Elkins to return.

AN EXERCISE IN LOGIC . . . . Page 113

Only statements (3) and (5) are necessarily true.

THE ISLAND OF KO . . . . Page 114

If the inhabitant questioned were Red, his second re-
sponse·would have to be "Red." If he were Green, his
second response would have to be a lie, "Red." Therefore,
he must be a Half-Breed. His second response is therefore a lie, so his first response is true. Tom is the name of
the Half-Breed.

Tom's third response must be true. Therefore, Dick
is the Red. Obviously, Harry must be the Green.

THE ESCAPING PRISONER . . . . Page 115

When the guards catch up to the prisoner, they will have
traveled the same distance, d, as the prisoner. If the time
it takes for the guards to travel distance d is represented
by t, then the time it takes the prisoner to travel distance d
is $t + \frac{1}{2}$ (because the prisoner had a half hour's head
start).

So, we have two equations:
$$4 \text{ mph (guards' speed)} \times t = d$$
$$3 \text{ mph (prisoner's speed)} \times (t + \tfrac{1}{2}) = d$$

Clearly, $4 \text{ mph} \times t = 3 \text{ mph} \times (t + \tfrac{1}{2})$
$$t = 1\tfrac{1}{2} \text{ hours}$$

In one and a half hours, the dog, traveling at 12 mph,
will cover 18 miles.

THE TWO STUDENTS . . . . Page 116

They were two of a set of triplets.

FIVE MASTERS . . . . Page 117

Each girl got two artists right, the five in order being:
(1) Degas; (2) Matisse; (3) Renoir; (4) Picasso; (5)
Klee.